LE D1233271

Where The Wind Blew Free

Tales of Young Westerners

☆ GENE JONES

Where The

Wind Blew Free

☼ *Tales of Young Westerners*

W. W. NORTON & COMPANY • INC • NEW YORK

This book is
for my son Hugh

Copyright © 1967 by Gene Jones
First Edition
Library of Congress Catalog Card No. 67-15443
All Rights Reserved
Published simultaneously in Canada by
George J. McLeod Limited, Toronto
Printed in the United States of America
1   2   3   4   5   6   7   8   9   0

Contents

Acknowledgments

For their help in the preparation of this book, many thanks are due to Mary Walker and Margaret Ashenden of the United Church Board for World Ministries who let me read the original letters and journals from Brainerd and Union Missions and to the staff of the Houghton Library at Harvard where these documents are deposited; also particularly to Helen D. Willard, curator of the great Harvard Theatre Collection who showed me its treasury of items on Johnny Baker and Buffalo Bill's Wild West; Richard I. Frost of the Buffalo Bill Museum, Cody, Wyoming; Jim Guadagno of the Museum of the American Indian, Heye Foundation; and the staff of the American History Room at the New York Public Library.

I am also grateful to Ruth Mortimer and to John Benedict for their aid, and especially to my dear friend the late Edwin V. Burkholder, whose advice and encouragement led me to write the stories in this book.

Foreword

Westward, beyond the Mississippi, feel the space, hear the silence, touch the wind . . .

Earth is endless, sky boundless, the body unpressed in an open universe. The space is so vast it makes even the long trails no more than tiny threads linking one people with another, mountain people with seashore people, men of the pueblos with warriors of the Plains.

In the huge silence of earth and sky, the wind's voice is magnified. Wind in summer rustles softly over the prairies, riffling the grassy sea. It hisses, raked by the spines of the cactus. It soughs in scrub oak and jack pine. In winter the howl of the norther is so huge, such madness of sound, it can only be god's voice raised in anger in that bitter, angry time of year.

Time was when the wind blew unhampered across America, countless years of time when scattered people of desert, shore, and plain sang praise to their gods for the spacious earth they loved, not knowing their time as free men was running out and the virgin land would no longer be theirs.

Fair-skinned warriors rode up from the south on strange new beasts called horses, rode through the pueblos and far on into the buffalo plains, searching, cajoling, threatening the people for a yellow metal they did not have. And after the fair, hairy warriors came brown-robed men preaching at the people that they must give up their good gods of earth and sky and accept one alien god, a god, said the preachers, of peace and mercy and love. These teachings, the people noted, were not practiced by the bearded warriors with their horses and shiny armor and long knives.

In time, pale-faced men came upon them from all directions, from the north in search of furs, from the east in ox-drawn wagon trains, even to the western shores in great winged canoes. They brought the people metal pots and bright cloth and beads. They brought firesticks that shot arrows without shafts, and liquor that put ruinous fires in the blood, and sicknesses that made whole villages die.

On every side the people were assaulted by these pale-skinned alien men with new ways of life and death, new gods and devils. Some of them came as friends and some turned out to be enemies, but in either case the people forgot the sound of silence and peace in their domain. Space closed in about them and time grew short. In fear, they fought the encroachment of the powerful fair strangers, who came in such flowing tides that the trails were like rivers in spate, the old trails that had been tiny streams linking one people with another.

These trails became famous roads in American history: the Oregon Trail, for example, the Natchez Trace, the Gila Trail. They are studded with famous landmarks, Chimney Rock, the Platte River crossings, South Pass, the Blue Mountains.

There is another road, nameless, a road of events in history that happened on those well-known trails and in the vast stretches of mountain and plain between them, and it led at the least to compromise, at best to a peaceful understanding between red men and white on how they would live together. It is a long road, going a hundred years in time from Horseshoe Bend to Wounded Knee. Its landmarks are the Trail of Tears, the Green River rendezvous of the mountain men, the California Gold Rush, the Indian Wars—all such events of the westward movement that transformed the middle of North America into the modern United States.

But the names of events and names on the land mean little until we know something of the lives of people who were involved in those events and lived on the land, or at least traveled across it.

The young westerners in this book did not know they were part of a great movement in history. They thought of their lives as sometimes adventuresome, sometimes fun, occasionally dull. Some were trying to make a new country into home, others trying to keep their old homes from being destroyed. Some of them had happy adventures, but along the way at times pretty frightful things happened to them, and some few, unhappily, never did get home.

John Osage Ross and Baptiste Charbonneau were the children of Indian people with roots deep in the land, and they were bewildered by the race prejudice and peculiar civilized captivities that uprooted them and turned them into displaced people. There is no record of Ross after he returned to his people. No one knows how life turned out for him. Charbonneau, we know, ultimately came to terms with the varied worlds of his experience by living and dying, as he wished, among his mother's people.

In contrast, Cynthia Ann Parker, Mo-keen, and perhaps Lizzie Fletcher, all found that they could sink deeper roots in Indian foster homes than any they had in their own families. Return to her real family was death to Cynthia Ann. Mo-keen the Mexican boy and Lizzie the English girl never had to suffer that second captivity, although both experienced the disintegration of the old Plains life and the transition to a shabby existence on reservations set up by white men.

For Johnny King, as for Olive and Mary Ann Oatman and the four German girls, the excitement and fun of life in a new country was disrupted by the most terrible of adventures, the brutal and sudden loss of their families, which left them alone in hostile hands. Out of that experience each made a choice as to whether a new home in the west was worth the struggle and losses it had cost them. Johnny King and Olive Oatman returned to live in eastern states, but the German sisters married and spent the rest of their days in the west.

Bill Tilghman and Johnny Baker stand apart from the others in these stories in that they saw, and apparently knew they were seeing, important transitions in American life. Tilghman helped kill off the buffalo herds and knew he was helping to alter life on the Plains, as he knew the railroad and town builders were doing. Had he been an articulate man he might well have said, Manifest Destiny is being fulfilled here and none of us want to stop its course. Progress is a pleasant sight.

Johnny Baker, on the other hand, was a man of great heart to whom the merciless course of Progress looked decidedly unfriendly. For a time he helped Buffalo Bill Cody preserve the excitement and glamour of the frontier they had both known as children. But Baker understood that that way of life was lost, and he was doubtless one of the few men of his time who could explain to Indians that Progress was a harsh master with whom any dealings must result in compromise. His talent for diplomacy was a result of this knowledge, learned in the world-in-microcosm in which he grew up—Buffalo Bill's Wild West Show. The larger world, he found, is after all a kind of stage, and if the men and women on it are not broken by the business of the show so that they end bitter and misanthropic, then they may finally learn the satisfactory compromise of tolerance and goodwill toward all the other actors in the play of life.

"I was born upon the prairie, where the wind blew free and there was nothing to break the light of the sun. I was born where there were no enclosures and everything drew a free breath. I want to die there and not within walls. I know every stream and every wood . . . . I have hunted and lived over that country. I live like my fathers before me and like them I live happily."

> Ten Bears, Comanche, spoke these words at the Council of Medicine Lodge Creek in 1867.

✵ *A restless urge to move on to new sights, new experiences, new homes, had been stirring American pulses long before the Revolutionary War, and it stirred them more strongly still when the second war with England ended in 1815. After so much fighting for their country, the new-forged Americans wanted to move around in it.*

They looked westward: that was the way to move. Expansion was the leading idea of those days. Americans felt crowded in their Atlantic shore states. Get out where a man could breathe free, they said. Get the Indians out of the way, build your cabin, put down crops. White man's civilization, that's what this country is for.

They spread to the Mississippi, then beyond. Out there was Mr. Jefferson's Louisiana Purchase to explore, claim, settle, and make use of. First in a trickle, then in a stream emigrants moved west, on horseback or afoot, trudging along trails with their great white-topped Conestoga wagons, or letting the wheels make new ones. They poled up rivers on flatboats, keelboats, rafts, even went on the new steamboats paddle-splashing as far upstream as their pilots dared. But however these Americans traveled—walking, wagoning, riding, boating—it was westward they moved, drawn by the magnet in the sunset.

All kinds of people made up the new frontier population. In Arkansas Territory, for example, there were settlers who wanted land to farm, there were adventurers and criminals who could no longer stay in the States (since states had courts and laws to hang them), there were soldiers, merchants, missionaries, and Indians. Arkansas was Indian country, originally the homeland of the great Osage tribe. The missionaries came to turn them into law-abiding Christian farmers, as they had successfully done among the Cherokees in Georgia and Tennessee.

The government, however, developed a policy of Indian removal in the 1820's and 1830's, which forced the Cherokees and other southeastern tribes to re-settle west of the Mississippi, so that white planters could take over their lands. This removal to Arkansas created an explosive situation there.

The Osages, a proud and powerful tribe, were put in a position of conflict, not with whites (with whom they got along well), but with other Indians. The Cherokees, insecure in their new homes, clung tenaciously to what land they could hold, and fought back. For years the struggle wore on, from the time of the first removal of Cherokees after the War of 1812 to the days of the Mexican War, when both Osages and the tribes from the east were settled on reservations.

No-People Boy

In Grah-Mo's town the little Osage boy called Otter waked and heard the voices of the old men who led the morning prayers to Wah'Kon-Tah, the Great Mysteries of the earth. First they sang a prayer to the morning star, and the little boy knew that the people were waking and coming to the east-facing doors of their lodges. Voice by voice they joined the next prayer, the hymn to Grandfather the Sun.

Otter's mother stirred next to him and he thought of his father, out on the prairie with the other warriors who would be singing these same prayers right now. All the young men, all the Osage warriors, were gone from the town with Grah-Mo the chief on the great autumn buffalo hunt. In his dreamy state of half-waking the boy followed the words of the song for Grandfather, whose light began to outline the lodge door.

Then his small body jerked against his mother's with a start of terror. War whoops shattered the prayers, women's screams broke the morning calm in every part of the town, dogs whined. The old men's voices died, hidden by the screams and gunshots and the shouting of strange warriors.

Suddenly awake, his mother clutched Otter and his younger sister awkwardly up into her arms. With his older sister following, they hurried out of the lodge and down the street that sloped to the river, since their lodge was on the side of the town nearest the river. Mother and children found themselves in the midst of a panicked crowd, people running in every direction. Many had started for the hill above the town, but seeing that the worst of the slaughter was taking place there, they tried to turn back and hide in the dense growth along the river's edge. The attack had been so unexpected, so sudden, that no one knew which side of the town it had come from, which way to run for escape.

There was no way to escape. The attackers, Cherokees with a scattering of white criminals and adventurers among them, came from every side. Otter's mother, gasping with fear, struggled past the last neat row of lodges and into a clump of bushes where she cowered with her three children.

But hiding was useless. Suddenly two Cherokees separated the bushes with their muskets. Their shots caught the mother full in the breast. Her blood spattered the children as she fell back. One warrior jerked Otter and his older sister away. The other man took his younger sister and threw her on a horse nearby. She fell off, screamed and struggled and was put on it again. The horse was hurried away.

Otter watched, paralyzed with terror in a maelstrom of noise and movement. The lodges up on the slope were burning and they seemed to churn about in their flames. Everywhere he saw women, boys, girls, and old men bloody, dying, dead, their bodies strewn all the way down to the river. So many had fallen into the water that its color changed. What had been yellow milky-mud color turned pink from their blood. He was too frightened

[4]

and too small a boy to struggle with the Cherokee who dragged him away, holding him tightly as he mounted. The horse whinnied and stepped gingerly over bodies, but the warrior guided it on, out of the confusion and smoky air.

They rode past white men making piles of loot they had taken from the lodges. Clusters of riders forded the river, hurrying eastward away from the burning town. The Cherokees were slowed by their Osage prisoners and stolen horses, the renegade whites by the loads of buckskin clothes, buffalo robes, and other goods. Through the damp autumn woods the invaders hurried along the banks of the Arkansas, fearful that the Osage warriors would come back from their buffalo hunt before they could get away.

The Osage men did not learn of the attack until days later, however. They returned from hunting to find their homes destroyed, their wives and children murdered or missing. Everyone the men had left in Grah-Mo's town was either dead or taken captive. Every lodge had been fired, all the corn and other food they had harvested and stored was destroyed, every object of value was burned or stolen. They had much to mourn for, but the greatest loss to them was the children. All the children were gone. . . .

Otter, held in the saddle in front of his captor, thought the journey to the east would never end. Day after day they jogged on through the malarial river bottoms of Arkansas, then across the great river and over the hills of northern Mississippi, Alabama, and Georgia to the country of the eastern Cherokees. He grew so tired it was dif-

[5]

ficult not to whimper, but his older sister, riding another horse, looked at him sternly and her look said, Osage boys do not cry, even if they are only three years old. The warrior would not let Otter go to his sister and grumbled loudly when they talked together or to the other captive children. From time to time women or children they knew would disappear as a warrior with his prizes splintered off from the larger party in order to dispose of them at some nearby plantation. There were over a hundred prisoners, mostly young boys and girls, who sold well as slaves. The Cherokees had made the long trek for the sole purpose of selling captives and horses to their eastern kinsmen. They would be rich men when they got home to Arkansas Territory, where the United States government had settled them on land taken from the Osages.

Brainerd Mission (part of modern Chattanooga, Tennessee) was over six hundred miles east of Grah-Mo's town (now Claremore, Oklahoma), but even on that rugged frontier it was no more than a few weeks before news of the plunder and destruction of the Osage town reached the mission. Brainerd was the central station of a network of Presbyterian missions to the Cherokees in Georgia, South Carolina, Tennessee, and Alabama. From the outstations word of the Osage captives filtered in to the center.

Otter and his older sister were carried far beyond Brainerd into South Carolina. When the journey ended for the three-year-old boy and his thirteen-year-old sister, more than eight hundred miles from their Osage home, they were sold as slaves to a Cherokee plantation owner.

[6]

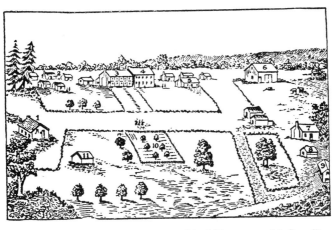

(1) Boys' School House   (5) Girls' School House   (9) Sawmill
(2) Boys' Cabin   (6) Barn   (10) Garden
(3) Mission House   (7) Farmer's House   (11) Graveyard
(4) Girls' House   (8) Carpenter's House

Brainerd Mission.

But their new home turned out to be temporary. They were settled no more than a year, from November 1817 to the autumn of 1818, when their owner began to talk of moving west to join his relatives in the Arkansas country. Perhaps the Osage children put him in mind of it. Their tribe was being pushed west onto the prairies. Commissioners from the Great White Father in Washington urged the Cherokees to emigrate west of the Mississippi and take up residence on Osage land. The Cherokee slaveowner sent a message to Brainerd Mission: He would bring the boy there to the missionaries' school on his way to Arkansas; the girl he would keep.

Immediately this message arrived giving a clue to the whereabouts of the two children, Reverend Ard Hoyt rode out from Brainerd with his son Milo in search of them. Hoyt, an enterprising and energetic man, was

[7]

superintendent of Brainerd Mission. He had high hopes of retrieving the children. He had already brought a little Osage girl in to Brainerd two months before, in September 1818. He did not know she was the sister of the two he was then setting out to look for.

But the result of the Hoyts' present search was bitter frustration. The Reverend and Milo found the children but could not persuade the owner to give them up. After a nine-day trip, three hundred miles of hard riding, they were back at Brainerd empty-handed. The missionaries had no way of forcing the man to part with his human chattels. When the Cherokee later decided to do so, he sold the little boy to another farmer for twenty dollars.

Another year later, in the autumn of 1819, Ard Hoyt's colleague Reverend William Chamberlin returned to Brainerd from a tour among the Cherokee towns with news that the boy had been sold again, this time for one hundred and fifty dollars to a man who lived on the Catawba River in central South Carolina. The missionaries decided they must make a more aggressive attempt to retrieve the child.

At this juncture a volunteer came forth offering to make the rescue. This was John Ross, the brilliant young Cherokee chieftain who was to become the greatest man of his people. Like the missionaries, he deplored the western Cherokees' vicious practice of town-raiding and child-stealing. Of mixed blood, Ross had the courage and strong character of his Scottish father. He was given a letter by Colonel Return J. Meigs, the Indian agent for the Cherokee country, which authorized him to bring the boy to Brainerd.

[8]

John Ross, the young Cherokee chief for whom John Osage Ross was named.

John Ross rode almost three hundred miles to the farm on the Catawba River where the boy was a slave. Dismounting, he approached the house cautiously so as not to be seen. No adults were about but the little boy, quite naked, was playing in the yard. He was not frightened at Ross' appearance. There was an immediate affinity between the bright-eyed little boy clothed in farmyard dust and the handsome young man in fine riding clothes, a spark of recognition between two open and forthright personalities. Ross took the boy up in his arms, explaining that he no longer had to stay a slave child in that place, but could go live where there were other free children and have warm clothes and good food, and learn about the white man's god in a school where he would speak English. Then the owner came out of the house.

At first he argued that Ross could not take the boy away as he had no clothes and was not ready for a trip. Then he denied the validity of Colonel Meigs' letter authorizing Ross to take the child. He made other feeble excuses. The two men exchanged sharp words. John Ross settled the argument by the simplest expedient: striding off with the boy in his arms, he mounted his horse and rode away.

Thirteen days after leaving Brainerd, Ross returned with a happy five-year-old passenger riding behind him. The white adults and Cherokee children of the mission school crowded around to greet the newcomer. He did not recognize his sister, but he saw a familiar face among the whites: it was Ard Hoyt, the stout, kind man who had come for him without success the year before. He was overwhelmed with the attention at first. The children chattered at him in Cherokee, some saying he was at home now and they were to be his people. But he saw they were all Cherokees and instinctively doubted them, particularly when some teased him, asking why he was naked and why he had no name and no people to claim him.

"Sah-juh!" said one. "Goose! Don't he look a scared goose? Let Goose be his name."

"No," Reverend Hoyt said, "not Sah-juh. Mr. Ross, you saved him—may we lend him your name? Let us call him John Osage Ross."

He was clothed and fed and taken to the meeting house where God was thanked for his deliverance. He was christened with his new name and sprinkled with baptismal water to make him a proper young Christian, and all were told to speak English to him so that his ear and tongue could more easily forget the difficult shaping of Osage and Cherokee words. Ard Hoyt adopted him, and his home was with the stout, smiling mission superintendent, his jolly wife, and their seven children.

When John Osage Ross was brought to his sister whom the missionaries had recovered the year before, the two children did not know each other. The boy was scrawny and unkempt. She was now six, a year older than he, and already transformed into a close approximation of a white child.

"My name is Lydia Carter now," she told him, "and we aren't to live as Indians any more." She had been carried off by a different band of Cherokee warriors, and her captor had sold her to an Indian farmer who lived only sixty miles from Brainerd. Her new master had had no intention of giving her up without satisfactory compensation. Once he offered to exchange her for a Negro slave child of the same age. The missionaries, disgusted at the Cherokees' traffic in stolen children, of course refused, but kept trying to reclaim her legally. Her plight became widely known. Mrs. Lydia Carter, a lady of Natchez who heard her story, offered one hundred dollars to ransom her. Late in September 1818 the exchange was finally made and the little girl came to live at Brainerd Mission. She was given Mrs. Carter's name. Young Reverend Chamberlin and his wife had taken her to live with them as their own daughter.

Lydia, with her year's experience in the customs of Brainerd Mission, was a strong pillar for her small brother to lean on. It was not easy for an Indian child, this process of learning to live as white people did—particularly such religious people. There were so many rules and strictures, most of which made no sense to him at all. "We don't do that, John," Lydia would say, and he would try not to repeat his unwitting mistake. She was always there to explain what she could and help him make the adjustment from Indian life. It was good to have someone of your own blood with you.

The other children persisted in calling him Sah-juh, the Goose. Lydia's Cherokee name was Te-tah-ke-zow-sky, which meant One Who Runs Too Fast to Be Taken. The Cherokee mission children felt a natural resentment against the Osage boy and girl who had been captives of their people and on whom the missionaries poured so much love and attention.

In a few days John began to feel at home in the big two-story mission house set in the center of the clearing. On the second floor lived the missionary families, the Hoyt family in two large rooms, and the Chamberlins with Lydia and their own baby daughter in another. On the ground floor were the large sitting room where the Indian girls spent much of their time learning to spin, weave, and sew, and the kitchen where they were taught cooking and candle molding. In addition there was a dining room with five long plank tables set with pewter plates, tin cups, and iron spoons. Everyone at the mission came there for meals.

John had no opportunity to explore the house and grounds as he would have liked—the missionaries deplored idle curiosity. The morning after his arrival, Reverend Hoyt took him across the clearing, past the neatly fenced orchard and garden plots, to the large building that was the boys' school house on weekdays and the meeting house on Sunday. During the year he was at Brainerd John probably gained little from the arithmetic and geography lessons, but he learned to read, write, and speak English (the mission scholars' record says he could "spell in two syllables"), and he absorbed the religious instruction. He had been too young before his unhappy Cherokee captivity to learn much of the immensely rich and complex religious system of the Osages. Now, stories of Hebrew prophets and heroes and heaven and hell were firmly implanted in the young mind, and a new Christian conscience was formed.

The best part of the religious lessons was hymn singing. All the children loved to sing the dramatic old songs.

[13]

Much of their English vocabulary was learned from such rousing favorites as "Watchman! tell us of the night" or the "Jubilee Hymn." Their young voices would fill the meeting house with:

> Hark! the songs of Jubilee
>   Loud as mighty thunders roar,
> Or the fulness of the sea
>   When it breaks upon the shore:—
> Hallelujah! for the Lord,
>   God omnipotent, shall reign;
> Hallelujah! let the word
>   Echo round the earth and main.

Life at Brainerd was simple and strictly controlled. Indian pupils were there to learn Protestant religious faith and elementary mechanical and intellectual skills of the white man. They were clothed, fed, and loved like the missionaries' own children. Frivolities were not tolerated—on one occasion, three boys were expelled for ball-playing. But life was peaceful at Brainerd in those years.

Sometimes there was a ruffle on the calm surface of the mission's life, as when President James Monroe and his entourage of army officers passed through in May 1819 on a tour of the western states. It was an impressive occasion for the children: here was the fabled Great White Father in their very midst, an awkward man with a gentle smile shaking their hands, patting their heads. The President was so impressed with Brainerd and its shining display of Indian scholars that he appropriated gov-

[14]

ernment funds to build a new dormitory and school house.

For John Osage Ross and Lydia Carter, it was a time of calm and security. For Lydia, it would be the longest such period in her life. The missionaries petted and spoiled her throughout her stay at Brainerd. Perhaps there was a special sympathy for them as orphan children. Both soon grew into happy members of the Brainerd family.

Then news came from the west, news that disrupted their lives again. War threatened between the Osages defending their hunting grounds and the encroaching Cherokees, and General James Miller, governor of Arkansas Territory, believed the threat could be dispelled if the Cherokees would return all the prisoners they had taken at Grah-Mo's town in 1817. General Miller arranged that the two tribes should meet with him on October 1, 1820. Then and there the Osage captives would be returned.

The news was a painful blow to the missionaries at Brainerd. Reverend Chamberlin in a letter of August 4, 1820, wrote: "My wife and myself are in trouble at present and wish your prayers. We expect every day to lose our dear Osage daughter . . . . I know they cannot take Lydia without orders from the President of the United States, but the man is waiting at the agency, probably for orders. We have not dared to tell her what the prospects are, though she got some hint of it among the children the other day. She ran to her mother in great surprise and said, 'Mother, they say some people have come after me; but mother won't let me go, will she?' Her mother could not answer her and it passed

[15]

off. . . . I think it will be as hard for us to part with her as if she were our own." The Hoyts felt just as strongly about losing John.

On the 21st of August John Rogers, the man who had been waiting at the Cherokee Agency, came with an official order to take away the two children and a troop of other prisoners who had been collected at Brainerd.

The usual order and serenity of the mission were shattered as it was turned into a temporary camp for these women and children. Horses, people, and traveling gear cluttered the buildings, the yards, the roadways. Everybody was on edge, the Cherokees resentful, the Osages anxious and uncertain, the missionaries unhappy at losing their Osage boy and girl. On the morning set for departure, Lydia added to the confusion by running away into the woods. Milo Hoyt lured her back with comforting words, but when she had to say good-bye to her mission family she burst into hysterical tears. John Osage Ross was less emotional, perhaps in part because he was told that if he would go without crying he could keep the horse with its bridle and saddle on which he was to ride to Arkansas.

There were other tears, for many of the Osage women and older girls had made successful marriages with Cherokee men and now were forced to leave their husbands. Finally the pathetic cavalcade was on its way in the steamy August heat. The long ride to Arkansas was made at the worst time of year. Soon more tears were shed over the pain and illnesses brought on by the journey. Lydia became feverish and by the time they crossed the Mississippi late in September she was seriously sick.

[16]

She and John were taken to John Rogers' house to be cared for.

Some of the prisoners were returned to the Osages, including the older sister of John and Lydia. When this girl was given to her people they showed what they thought of her captors by ripping her Cherokee clothes to shreds as they publicly, ceremonially, dressed her in proper Osage garments.

But on the whole the negotiations were a failure. The Cherokees made false accusations against the Osages and claims for damages that could not be paid, so that they would not have to return all the prisoners. Their arguments dragged on for five months, but still no decision was made about the fate of the two Osage children from Brainerd Mission. Governor James Miller learned of their situation during the winter. Fearing that they were unsafe with Rogers, who was a Cherokee, he had them taken in February 1821 to the home of Mrs. Persis Lovely, the widow of a man who had been for many years an agent and friend to the Osages.

More weary weeks followed, weeks of waiting as trying for the children as for Mrs. Lovely and Governor Miller. The governor saw the treaty negotiations disintegrate, as Mrs. Lovely, patient and motherly, watched over the fast-failing little girl and tried to keep John quietly occupied. Despite her care, Lydia grew sicker. She died, aged seven, on March 9, 1821.

Now John's welfare became a problem. Mrs. Lovely was an elderly lady who could not indefinitely keep an active six-year-old boy. The Cherokees refused to return him to the Osages, so Governor Miller sensibly took him away to his own home at Crystal Hill, near Little Rock. Like Ard Hoyt, Miller became a loving foster father to him. Busy as he was moving about the strife-torn territory trying to settle its problems, he took care to see that John went to school and was properly cared for.

In the summer of 1821, Governor Miller took a leave of absence and made a trip to his home in New Hampshire. To insure the boy's safety he took John Osage Ross with him. John must have quailed at the thought of another journey to another strange place. But this time he traveled in comfort with Governor Miller, and the excitement of seeing the white men's great eastern cities made up for some of the insecurity he felt. In Washington he was presented to President Monroe with formal ceremony, and in New England Miller's relatives and friends showered him with attentions. Once back in the governor's house at Crystal Hill, John settled down for a comparatively lengthy and tranquil period of time.

He went to school, he went to church, he learned to be a dutiful, respectful boy. His English became fluent and he remembered no Indian words at all. He had no contacts with Indians any more, other than seeing them at Little Rock or Fort Smith: drunken Miamis or Choctaws or Delawares begging in the streets, Cherokees imitating white men in their dress and obsequious manner, and the lordly, aloof Osages conspicuous for their height, their beauty, their dignity.

Governor Miller talked to John of his future at times, of how he was being prepared for what the governor called a productive Christian life. He could no longer spend much time with John. As his term of office wore on he

[18]

was kept busy constantly with the harassing administrative problems of his frontier territory. His own future plans were uncertain until, at the end of 1824, President Monroe appointed him Collector of the Port of Salem, Massachusetts. Miller prepared to leave the territory for his new appointment. John Osage Ross was then ten years old, old enough to be apprenticed to a trade that would support him when he grew up. Rather than uprooting him again, Miller arranged for his apprenticeship to a saddler in Arkansas. John's practical education would continue and he would be well cared for. Many white boys, he was told, wished they had such opportunities as his.

So John applied himself diligently to the saddler's trade, believing he could set up business one day for himself in one of Arkansas' growing towns. They were booming in the 1820's, the years of his youth. There was a sense of excitement, of movement, in the air. Conestoga wagons full of emigrants rumbled down the main land highway into the territory along Crowley's Ridge; in 1828 steamboats began making regular runs up the Arkansas River, carrying planters and their slaves, soldiers, curiosity seekers, good men and bad in greater numbers every day. It seemed an auspicious time and place for a young man who made saddles and bridles.

But John Osage Ross was an Indian. Any white man could see that at a glance. He grew into a tall and handsome young man, showing his Osage blood, for the Osages were the tallest and handsomest Indians in the country. His black hair was cut short, but his brown skin could not be disguised by the neat workman's clothes

nor by his Sunday-go-to-meeting suit. He worked as jour-
neyman with the master who had taught him his trade,
trimming and decorating the leather and shaping the
saddles just as his master did, but white men had doubts
about buying a saddle made by Indian hands.

Reverend William Requa, in his letter-report to the
mission board of December 12, 1836, wrote of educated
Osages he wanted on his staff at the mission colony he
was to establish on the new Osage reservation. The reverend's letter was enthusiastic about both the young
Osages and the new mission up north; he was writing
from Union Mission on the Neosho River in eastern Oklahoma, an old established center like Brainerd. One of
the Osage people was a young woman "willing and even
anxious," he wrote, "to go among her people and labour
for their good." Another was "a young man, taken captive when a child, but released and brought up by Governor Miller, who has learned the saddler's trade and
speaks only the English language, he is about being sent
back to his people."
Reverend Requa must have reflected long and seriously on these young people. The girl was all right. She
had been brought up at a mission school, but she had
maintained contact with her people, their language, their
ways of life. It would be easy for her to work among
them. John Osage Ross was in a different category altogether. He was twenty-three years old then. His speech
and manners were polished, his whole approach to life
was that of a well-educated tradesman, not an Indian.
Still, the reverend agreed, blood was thick, a place had to

be found for him since Indians were not allowed to live in white men's towns. It was better he should go to his own tribe.

Feeling ran high among white settlers around Union Mission. Their land claims were doubtful at best, according to law. But Arkansas was a state now, they shouted, white man's land: didn't Indians belong on reservations? So they got their way and the land. Government was moving the Osages to a new reservation out on the wind-swept prairie. Their agent said John had to go too. John did not speak the Osage tongue; he had been brought up as a white boy and had little in common with the people he was to live among. He knew none of them—he had not lived in an Indian household since he was four years old. But he was an Indian born: he had to go.

Temporarily, therefore, he had been sent to the missionaries who wanted educated Indians to work with them. They were closing up their missions in the Arkansas country—the Indians they had served were gone, driven from their ancestral lands—and Reverend Requa was deep in plans for the new mission colony among the Osages, farther north in what would one day be called Kansas. Union Mission, from which he wrote the letter mentioning John Osage Ross, was only twenty-odd miles east of Grah-Mo's now deserted town. There, Requa knew, John's life had begun, there he had seen horrors of slaughter and destruction. From there he was taken for a Cherokee slave, afterward to become a semi-genteel captive among white men. Would this new move merely put him in a new captivity, ironic because the Osages were his "own" people?

Surely not, thought Requa, surely they would make him welcome and happy and he would soon learn to be an Indian again.

But the reverend could not be sure. He remembered a chieftain called Tally who had left his two sons at the mission school only after strong persuasion. His people would ridicule him, Tally said, for letting his sons be brought up as white men, would make them outcasts from the tribe. The parting was sorrowful. Tally charged the missionaries, if they must take his sons, to turn them wholly into white men, not to come among the Osages again. Make them take off their moccasins, he said, and put on stockings and shoes, for they would never be Osage warriors.

Requa, looking at John Osage Ross in comparison to the Osage braves he was used to seeing at the mission and on the prairie, could understand Tally's concern. Still, he felt sure that educated Indians like John were the perfect connecting links between the missionaries and their own people, perfect instructors in white men's ways.

The situation of the Osage people was very bad. In his letters to the mission board Requa had written time and again of the harrassment and insecurity of the tribe, their towns destroyed, their hunting grounds overrun by whites and other Indians, the game—their staff of life— depleted. So bad was their condition that he thought it possible that "this unfortunate and degraded nation," as he called them, might die out completely. He was determined to do what he could to prevent that end.

He set to work with extraordinary ability and energy,

optimism and faith: boundless faith in his God and in the Indians he had come to serve. For four years, as long as removal of the Osages to a reservation had been talked of, he laid plans for the new mission colony, selecting his staff of white missionaries and Indian assistants. John Osage Ross was to be one of these. Requa explored the new reservation and located a fine site for the colony, "the management of which," he wrote enthusiastically, "is to devolve upon me." The move would be made early in 1837.

In March 1837, Requa was busy helping Osage families pack their belongings. John worked with him. Although the boy spoke no language but English, he was quick and would surely re-learn Osage in no time, and as a saddler, Requa wrote, "his trade if followed would be profitable to himself and useful to his people." The reverend added: "We hope that these educated Osages will yet be a blessing to their more ignorant and benighted countrymen."

He was never to know.

Hostilities erupted along the Osage frontier that spring; the tribe had been pushed to the breaking point. The country was flooded with emigrant Indians—mostly eastern Cherokees who had been forced off their lands, too, and driven like cattle along what they called the Trail of Tears. They were to settle in a proposed permanent Indian Territory west of Arkansas, in prairie country the Osages had already been pushed into.

The Osages had had enough. They pulled back from all but warlike contacts, refusing even to allow white missionaries on their reservation. The whites also gave up.

"All the brethren of the Osage mission," Reverend Requa wrote, "in consequence of blighted hopes and discouraging prospects, have left, and it seems as if it would be right under the present circumstances to abandon the mission entirely."

So Requa's career among the Osages ended in failure. But in his last days at Union Mission, defeated as he was, he sat in the empty mission house and wrote of his hope "that God will yet graciously regard the poor afflicted despised and forsaken Osages, and answer the many prayers that have been offered up for them. . . . He is not unmindful of our work and labour of love, but will crown our efforts ultimately with success among the heathen for ask of me, saith the Lord, & I will give thee the heathen for thine inheritance & the uttermost parts of the earth for thy possession . . . ."

No more is recorded of the life of John Osage Ross, and the very lack of record implies that he did not serve as Reverend Requa's deputy among the Osages. Possibly he was able to throw away his white man's stockings and shoes, put on moccasins, and become an Indian again. Perhaps he was claimed again by the band of his tribe that had lost him so long ago.

And perhaps when the time came, the chanters sang the prayers of dying, and the drums, weeping like the pulse of life, called to Wah' Kon-Tah, the Great Mysteries of earth, to take him. Perhaps the people of his band painted the tribal markings on his face and wrapped him in a blanket, properly, so he would not be lost in heaven and they would see him there and say, "Yes, he is one of *our* people."

[24]

✧ *The people of the United States believed that only they should dominate the land from Atlantic to Pacific. It was, they said, their Manifest Destiny to control the continent, or as much of it as they could acquire, to make their fortunes out of its furs, its gold, its land, to mold it into a white man's world of farms and cities.*

Lewis and Clark returned to St. Louis in 1806 from their exploring journey to the Pacific, the greatest of American adventures before Colonel Glenn soared into space, and of no less far-reaching consequences. Within a generation after those first explorers had given the young United States a tantalizing glimpse of its vast western domain, the land was being plundered of enormous riches.

The vanguard who blazed the trails were the mountain men of the 1820's and 1830's, fur trappers and traders important in American history not so much because they founded several fortunes (John Jacob Astor's, for one) by stripping western streams of beaver, but because they found paths that emigrants could travel in later years. Sometimes, after the fur trade collapsed, they also acted as guides along those trails.

Thus the fur trade was not only the first great business of the west, but the instrument of Manifest Destiny. Because the trade necessarily brought its men into contact with Indian tribes, it served a further purpose as an agent of Indian destruction by

[25]

introducing alcohol and diseases like smallpox among them. With such weapons, the white man could not fail to win the west. There were Indians to whom it was manifest even in those early days that the red man's destiny was not always to be lord of the mountains and the plains.

※ CHAPTER TWO

International American

From the supply cart he drove, the half-breed Charbonneau cast a glance at the wagons straggling out across the prairie. It was not a train of freight wagons for the Indian trade nor of settlers on the great migration of that year, 1843. This train was the "pleasure party" of the wealthy Scottish sportsman Sir William Drummond Stewart, a hunting and sightseeing jaunt from St. Louis to the Rocky Mountains. In the motley variety of Sir William's guests—gentlemen of New Orleans and St. Louis, their servants or slaves, priests, botanists, journalists—Baptiste Charbonneau found one more interesting than all the others: a lad of eighteen, sturdy and tall, a fair boy with carrot-red hair who was, Charbonneau well knew, the image of his father.

Everyone liked the boy, Charbonneau saw that, and not only Sir William's many prominent guests. A journalist with the party wrote: "All the Indians looked with great curiosity upon young Jefferson Clark, who was with

us, they recognizing the boy's resemblance to his father—
the unmistakable red hair and benevolent features of the
great explorer." Jefferson's father was "the famous pio-
neer, Clark," as the journalist had called him, William
Clark, friend to the Indians, governor of Missouri, and
once, long ago, foster father of Baptiste Charbonneau.

He was not one to record his feelings, this half-breed
Charbonneau (but well he could have—he was better educated than most of the gentlemen in the Stewart party),
so none can say whether he was bitter or amused at the
attention Jeff Clark drew. He was a mature man, nearly
forty then. He had long since put his childhood away into
the hazy place of memories. He looked back most fondly
at the first years he could remember, in St. Louis, then a
frontier village thrusting the woods back from the Mississippi. In those days William Clark was governor of
the territory and great man of those parts, the country's
hero, and the tall, stern, just, and fatherly man who called
Baptiste Charbonneau his boy Pomp.

Pomp's real father was Toussaint Charbonneau, trader
to the Indians of the Upper Missouri country, and his
mother the Shoshoni woman Sacagawea. He was born
February 11, 1805, and a few weeks later his parents had
set off with the Lewis and Clark expedition across the
Shining Mountains, the Rockies. He was carried in a cradle board on his mother's back all the way to the Pacific
and back again to the Hidatsa village where they lived.
Sacagawea's baby so charmed the Redhead Captain, as
she called William Clark, that he wanted to adopt the
boy.

Even before the captain reached St. Louis at the end of

[27]

William Clark, the great explorer who wanted to adopt young Baptiste Charbonneau.

the expedition in September 1806, he wrote to the parents: "As to your little son (my boy Pomp) you well know my fondness for him and my anxiety to take and raise him as my own child. I once more tell you if you will bring your son Baptiste to me, I will educate him and treat him as my own child. . . . with anxious expectations of seeing my little dancing boy Baptiste, I shall remain your friend, William Clark."

So the half-breed boy with his Indian mother and French father came to live in St. Louis. When he was six his parents returned to their Indian home and left him entirely in Governor Clark's charge. Then his education began in earnest. In St. Louis there were good masters for young scholars like Pomp: sometimes a Protestant minister or a Catholic priest, sometimes an everyday schoolmaster. He learned English and French and geography, Spanish and arithmetic, and how to write in a fine flowing hand. The Indians who came to talk with their friend the red-haired governor taught him their dialects and sign language, and Clark taught him something about dealing with Indians. Pomp even learned fencing and the fashionable European ballroom dances, from a master who taught both.

At the age of eleven he was a soundly educated boy and a graceful young gentleman. Then Pomp's father sent for him, and the course of his life changed radically.

He had grown up as Governor Clark's boy Pomp in the warmth and security of a home in the white man's bustling river town. Now he was to travel far northwest up the great Missouri and live as an Indian boy. It could not have been easy to part with the foster father he knew and loved to go to his own father, a stranger who lived a

[29]

strange rough life in a distant country, and whom he had not seen since he was little more than a baby.

Passage was arranged for Pomp on a keelboat. The governor put him aboard and they said good-bye. The crowd on the levee waved and shouted as the boatmen warped the craft out into the Mississippi. He looked back until St. Louis was lost to sight. Finally they pulled into the broad muddy mouth of the Missouri.

It was a long journey, but exciting to the eleven-year-old boy. Sometimes the sail was used; sometimes the men poled the boat, or rowed; sometimes the cordelle, a tow rope attached to the top of the mast, was thrown out and the men leaped ashore to pull the boat against the treacherous shifting current, singing as they tugged:

> Some row up and some row down,
>   All the way to Shawnee Town,
> Pull away, pull away,
>   Pull away to Shawnee Town!

There was much traffic on the river in its lower reaches. Frequently Baptiste recognized landmarks from Governor Clark's descriptions. After they had passed Fort Osage and the shabby village of Independence, settlements were fewer. At Council Bluffs half the trip was done. At Fort Manuel in the Dakota country, Baptiste, in a blue mood, looked for the grave of his mother Sacagawea; it was here, he knew, that she had died four years before, in December 1812. A few days later they sighted the towns of the earth-house people and his destination was reached.

[30]

Looking up, he saw the two Mandan villages spread along the low bluffs on his right. The domed tops of great earth lodges were visible behind the log palisades surrounding each town. Between the bluffs and the river's edge were cornfields cultivated by the women. Then his attention was drawn to his left, to the west side of the Missouri where a smaller stream emptied into it. It was the Knife River and beside it were the round earth houses of the Hidatsa town where Toussaint Charbonneau lived. The keelboat was beached and Baptiste, with some trepidation, trudged up the hill to meet his father.

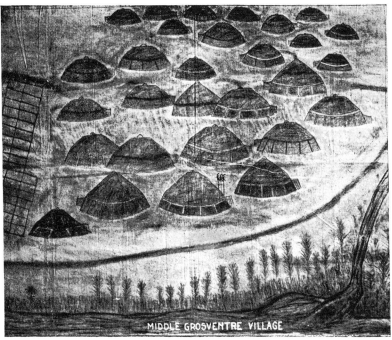

An Indian drawing of the Hidatsa village on the Knife River where Baptiste went to live with his father.

Old Toussaint had come as a trader to live among these river tribes long, long ago ("When I first came on this river," he would say to his son, "it was so small I could straddle it!"), and few men knew the ways of the tribes as well as he. He had found life good there and wanted Baptiste to have a similar career.

When the boy first came to him he said, "It is time now for you to be with me, your true father, and put away childish things. Soon I will be old and you will be a man. The redhead governor gave you book-learning, Baptiste, yes? Now I will give you life-learning."

It was puzzling, the decisions white fathers made, but he accepted his true father's words, only answering, "Yes, mon père." Then he said, "You call me only Baptiste. Why did he always call me Pomp?"

Toussaint said, "Hah, Pomp. Your mother called you so. In Shoshoni tongue Pomp is the word for a first-born son, as you were. So the redhead called you that too. He named a mountain Pomp for you."

"Oh, yes! Pomp's Tower." The boy glowed with pride. "The governor says it will be a memorial to my first journey long after I make my last one."

"Those captains," Toussaint said, "they made many memorials. They named every river, every mountain. A creek they called after me, Charbonneau, a river for your mother, a mountain for you—when we came to that big butte on the Yellowstone, Clark said 'Let's call that Pomp's Tower.' Eh voilà, someday you go to see it."

"Yes. Someday I'll go to my mother's people too."

Meanwhile there were other journeys, trading expeditions with his father that lasted from spring to fall. Sometimes they went to the nearby Mandans and Arikaras, sometimes much farther, upriver to the Assiniboins or Crees or even some Blackfoot bands if they were not at war, or into Absaroka, the country of the Crows. Beads, hatchets, kettles, knives, and awls, packets of vermilion for war paint, blankets, guns—Baptiste learned their value in terms of the magnificent beaver, otter, and mink pelts and buffalo robes the Indians brought to the trader in exchange. He learned to trade horses as well, and to manage a string of pack horses or mules on the plains or mountain trails.

In winter, or whenever they were not on a trading trip, home was a great Hidatsa earth lodge. It was a single circular room, fifty feet in diameter, a structure of log posts and rafters over which willow poles were laid tight together for walls and ceiling, with a layer of grass thatch next and hard-packed earth six inches deep over that. In the center was the fireplace with its smokehole above, open to the sky in the top of the earthen dome. Around the sides curtained beds were built into the wall and racks and shelves held Toussaint's pack saddles and other gear. Just inside the entrance door on its left was a small corral for horses.

But not all Baptiste's time was spent in the lodge or working with his father. Without hesitation, he took to an Indian boy's life. He was a physically small boy, agile and good at games. He wrestled, rode the plains, and hunted with Hidatsa and Mandan boys, picked up their dialects and learned their games of shinny and throwing darts at a rolling hoop. He swam with them in the muddy Missouri and teased the girls as they went down to culti-

[33]

vate the cornfields along the river.

He came to be clever at trading, quick to drive a bargain as his father was; he could chatter with white men in French, English, or Spanish, and with red men in several tongues as well as their sign language. Because his Indian blood showed in his dark features and glossy straight black hair, the Indians accepted him as one of them. And despite his upbringing in the frontier elegance of St. Louis society, he felt at home in the rough, primitive life of the Indian towns.

When he was eighteen, Baptiste left a trading career and made a journey across the prairies, which was a turning point in his life.

In that summer of 1823 the half-breed boy took a fur-laden pirogue downriver to Chouteau's trading village at the mouth of the Kansas River. At that colorful settlement, alive with the comings and goings of bearded, buckskinned fur trappers and St. Louis businessmen in beaver hats and city clothes, an adventurous young traveler from Europe stopped, looking for a guide and interpreter to travel the prairies with him. He was a royal highness, Paul Wilhelm Friedrich, Prince of the German state of Württemberg. He was then twenty-five, by chance a nobleman, by choice a student of science and humanity. His democratic attitudes were out of place in the royal court of his birth. Later he would write: "In the atmosphere of a palace I would feel like a wild thing . . . imprisoned in a gilded cage . . . and my heart would never cease to hunger for the vast silent places and the simple life among free unaffected children of nature."

The two young men were friends immediately they

met. No other guide would suit Prince Paul so well, he was sure, no better interpreter could be found to translate the Indian tongues and language of signs into the European languages he knew. And his choice was the right one. Baptiste conducted the tour imaginatively and with enthusiasm, to the admiration of his princely employer. Plants and animals of the plains and prairies were searched out for the prince's study and examples selected to take home to Württemberg with him. They hunted buffalo; they talked with Indians in tepee villages and saw their great summer Sun Dance festivals. Prince Paul thought it a glorious tour. Baptiste, for the first time since his childhood, had a literate, well-educated friend.

The experience brought out the best in him, a talent for conversation, a sparkle of wit and charm in his flashing black eyes. Prince Paul was delighted with his protégé. When the tour ended in the autumn of 1823, he was determined not to be parted from Baptiste.

"Come to Europe with me," he said.

Baptiste considered. "Shall I be your jester at court, prince?"

"No. My companion," Paul said. "My friend. There is no jester at my court."

It was too attractive an offer to pass by. In late October they were in St. Louis where Baptiste had the pleasure not only of a reunion with Governor William Clark but also of presenting himself as a successful young man chosen to be the companion of a wealthy and discriminating European nobleman. Clark must have felt a surge of pride for the handsome young man who had once been his boy Pomp.

[35]

On November 3, Prince Paul and Baptiste began a lei-surely trip down the Mississippi. At New Orleans they embarked on the brig *Smyrna* which landed at Havre in February 1824.

The journey across Europe was a delightful revelation to Baptiste. So many people crowded into such a succes-sion of cities, farms, and towns—nothing could be more different from the open land and sparse settlements of America. He was surrounded with people here always, and their houses astonished him. At home most dwell-ings of both white men and Indians were temporary and replaceable, settler's shanty or skin tepee. In Europe the houses were solid, permanent, many of them ancient and built for the ages.

Their carriage rolled across France and the Rhineland and brought them in a few weeks to Stuttgart, capital of the state of Württemberg. From the vineyards and wooded hills of south Germany they entered the cobbled streets of the old town. Here Prince Paul was welcomed by his people; but they did not stay in the city, for the prince's home was a small castle thirty miles farther.

Some months were spent installing Prince Paul's col-lection of trophies and curiosities from America in the castle, and in teaching Baptiste German and presenting him to the court of Württemberg. There was after all some danger of his being looked on as a jester in the royal household: an Indian from America was a curiosity, but an educated half-breed Indian was an exotic of consid-erable note in a provincial German court. It was a mark of honor to be seated next him at state dinners. Everyone marveled at his witty conversation.

But Prince Paul refused to stay in Württemberg long, and when he traveled Baptiste went with him. The prince loved to travel. The discomforts, even dangers, of far places were a challenge to him. He wanted to see and explore as much as possible before he was required to settle into the stuffy official life of the court.

They traveled in Germany until Baptiste had a thorough command of the language. Then their journeys extended into France and finally to England. Baptiste acquired all the manners of a gentleman as he was introduced into noble and fashionable salons across half of Europe. They moved in a leisurely way, stopping sometimes in cities or resort towns. Occasionally they were invited to the great country house of some noble relative or acquaintance of Paul's. This kind of travel was instructive for Baptiste, but not at all to Paul's taste. After a couple of years in Europe he wanted a more adventurous outing.

America was too far away, but there was Africa. European travelers were beginning to explore that continent in increasing numbers in the 1820's. Prince Paul decided to examine only the northern rim, the desert. For weeks on end they studied the ancient mysteries of timeless, barbaric cities—Algiers, Tunis, Oran—which seemed as old as the desert and the sea they lay between. Then they rode on camelback with caravans that took them far into the desert, or into the Atlas to hunt black-maned desert lions.

When they sailed back across the Mediterranean and came again to Württemberg, Prince Paul's family had decided it was time for him to marry. The African trip was the last for a while. A marriage was arranged, as was the custom in royal houses, and the wedding took place. In a year's time Prince Paul was a father. He had done his duty, given his branch of the royal house an heir. Now he could go journeying again, once more to America.

"Shall I take you home, Baptiste?" he said.

Home. Where was it? Home had been so many places to him. "America, you mean? Yes," he said, considering what he might do when he was no longer with Prince Paul, "yes, let me go home to America."

He was twenty-three years old; he had been traveling most of those years. It was good to see the world, but there were great distances to travel in America, after all. He thought of the vast Plains with their broad, shallow rivers, of the snow-peaked Shining Mountains, of the Indians, his people. Five years in Europe had ripened and matured him, but there were no attachments to hold him in that crowded urban world.

By the end of that year, 1829, they were in St. Louis. Governor William Clark, sixty years old, his famous red hair gone white, wrote a passport for Prince Paul's trip through the Indian country. Then, in his last known contact with the young man who had been his boy Pomp, he found Baptiste a position with the powerful American Fur Company.

During their passage up the Missouri, Baptiste Charbonneau and Prince Paul of Württemberg said their farewells. They were not to meet again. The royal tourist continued his explorations without a companion. Charbonneau, reverting to the primitive life of the wilderness, became a fur trapper in the Rockies, one of that legen-

[38]

dary breed of mountain men who were the lifeblood of the fur trade in its last heyday and trailmakers for the generations of emigrants to come.

They were heroic men, those mountain trappers. More Indian than the Indians—for their lives and work depended on an Indianlike knowledge of animals, weather, the country they worked, an ability to read any "sign"—they wore buckskin clothes made and decorated by Indian women, they borrowed the Indian's nomadic way of life and some of his religion, his foods, and frequently his women for wives. Some mountain men, like Jim Bridger and Kit Carson, were later famous as scouts, but they were first famous for their exploits as trappers, Indian fighters, and trail finders. Charbonneau was not the least among them: "It was said that Charbenau was the best man on foot on the plains or in the Rocky Mountains," commented a diary of the early 1840's.

In the fall of the year the fur company would send him out with a brigade of twenty or thirty men who explored the mountain streams for signs of beaver, set their traps, and collected the pelts. When the streams froze solid and snows prevented their moving about, they settled into winter quarters, sometimes with friendly Indians, sometimes just the brigade, in a spot like Brown's Hole or Bayou Salade protected from the worst of the winter's storms. The spring thaw allowed them to trap beaver again, then in early summer the brigade set off with their season's catch for the annual trapper's rendezvous at some pre-arranged site like Pierre's Hole, or the magnificent upper valley of the Green River. The company supply train from St. Louis brought the men their yearly wages and equipment: new traps, powder and balls for their rifles, clothing, such luxuries as coffee, tobacco and sugar, and whiskey. As soon as they could exchange their pay for supplies the party began—for to the mountain men the rendezvous was incidentally a business exchange, a great trade fair, but mainly a month's vacation after a year of hard labor and exposure to the elements, hostile Indians, and grizzly bears.

Bands of friendly Indians, the Shoshonis, paraded in with gorgeous display and set up their tepees. Trappers— French Canadians or Missourians, Mexicans or Virginians, or half-breeds like Baptiste Charbonneau—all came together at the rendezvous after a year scattered over thousands of square miles. It was a grand reunion. The boys let go with a whoop and a holler: horse races and foot races, tall tales, wrestling and shooting matches, herculean gambling and drinking bouts were the order of the day, often ending in serious brawls. Once everybody had let off enough steam they cleared out to get on with the next fall hunt.

Fifteen years, the best years of his young manhood, Baptiste spent as a mountain man. Standing in the icy water of a mountain stream to plant beaver traps, that was an everyday thing for him, and hunting game to feed the brigade he traveled with, and going hungry when he could find no deer, no buffalo. Those were the last great years of the fur trade. The beaver was nearly exterminated, then finally saved from extinction by a simple change in fashion, the new silk hats that superseded beaver-felt hats in the 1840's. Charbonneau moved south and went to work as a hunter and roustabout for the firm that owned Bent's Fort, the great castle of adobe bricks at the southeastern edge of the Rocky Mountains on the Arkansas River (then the boundary between Mexico and the United States).

He was remembered from those years for qualities other than his talents as a mountain man and hunter. "There was a quaint humor and shrewdness in his conversation," a friend noted, "so garbed with intelligence and perspicuity, that he at once insinuated himself into the good graces of his listeners, and commanded their admiration and respect...." That was written in August 1842 when Baptiste was camped on an island in the shallow Platte River, waiting for high water to float a boatload of furs down to the Missouri and on to St. Louis. Comparing himself to Napoleon in exile, he called the island St. Helena. The fur-laden boat was stuck for two months there but the camp was well supplied. When travelers stopped to pass a day or two, Baptiste received them hospitably with mint juleps, civilized conversation, and a meal that included boiled buffalo tongue and coffee—a famous guest, the army explorer John C. Frémont, added: "with the luxury of sugar."

Finally released from his summery exile on the Platte, Baptiste got his boat full of furs to St. Louis. When spring came in 1843, he hired out to drive a cart on Sir William Drummond Stewart's pleasure party to the mountains.

At Westport Landing on the Missouri, now part of Kansas City, Sir William Stewart's touring party came to an end in October 1843. Charbonneau saw the last of the

Scottish lord and his guests, the city gentlemen, and of William Clark's red-haired son, Jeff.

"What will you do now, old man?" he was asked.

"Go to the mountains, I think."

"An educated man like you? Come to St. Louis, make something of yourself."

"I don't belong in cities. I am half-breed, you know, not white. I go back there. To my mother's people, perhaps."

He took the Santa Fe Trail west. For a time he worked again as a hunter supplying buffalo meat for Bent's Fort. In 1845 the United States army was sending out exploring parties into territory it would soon take from Mexico. Charbonneau was praised for his skill in guiding an expedition from Bent's Fort south to the Canadian River and eastward into Texas.

The Mexican War began early in 1846, disrupting trade and everyday life throughout the southwest. In the autumn Charbonneau the army guide was in Santa Fe, soon after United States soldiers had occupied the graceful old city. Troops were being sent on from there to take over California from the crumbling Mexican government. Guides were needed, frontiersmen who could find paths for the army through desert and mountains to the sea. Charbonneau signed on.

He guided the famous Mormon Battalion through an arduous passage, the cruel winter desert of the southwest. Men sickened on alkaline water and short rations. More than once a shallow pit was scratched in the hard soil and rocks piled over the grave to keep coyotes from disinterring the body. In January 1847 the battalion straggled into San Diego.

[42]

In the chaos of transition from Mexican to American rule in California, Baptiste Charbonneau was a valuable man. As an American, the American invaders trusted him; but he could talk with and understand the Mexicans, who liked him; furthermore, he was half Indian and the masses of Indians, suddenly freed from their slavelike subjection on the great ranchos and mission holdings, felt he was one of them, could help them. His services as translator and settler of disputes between hotheaded Californians and brutal frontier soldiers were required often. Then in November 1847 he was honored by the people of the village of San Luis Rey, near San Diego, who asked him to become their *alcalde*, or mayor.

San Luis Rey de Francia had been a mission village, that is, a mission church and its buildings with a collec-

San Luis Rey in a lithograph made shortly before the Americans came and Charbonneau was made alcalde; *behind the arcade at left the Indians lived and worked for the padres of the mission.*

[43]

tion of Indian dwellings built around it. Three thousand Indians—Luiseños they were called, their old tribal name forgotten—lived in the town, their welfare administered by a handful of Californians. It seemed a calm and friendly town when Baptiste took over its affairs. In a few months he saw it with different eyes.

The California Indians had been wrenched from one way of life to another three times in a hundred years, first from their fine free aboriginal ways to the confined routine of the new missions in the eighteenth century; then when Mexico freed herself from Spain in 1821 they lost the protection of the missions; finally the blustering Americans arrived and destroyed what little security they had left. Then the wind blew revolt whispering over the hills where the Luiseños had once been free men and through the thatched roofs of the adobe huts that clustered around the mission church and through the deserted workshops where padres had kept the Luiseños busy learning the white man's crafts and religion.

Rebellion: the conspiracy developed in the spring of 1848. Spaniards had been bad and Mexicans worse masters, but Americans were the worst beasts of all. Destroy these whites or they will destroy us, the Luiseños prophesied. Only the *alcalde* was not white. His blood was theirs: Indian. He would understand.

Confronted with rumors, Baptiste was shocked to learn that the Luiseños had implicated him in their plans. Immediately he investigated, tried to search out the Indians who had used his name and bring them to trial. But a finger had been pointed at him; he was now suspect to the United States occupation authorities.

[44]

Baptiste spoke out in his own defense and there were friends who spoke for him. To prove his honor, he brought his eight-month career as *alcalde* of San Luis Rey to an end. Because of his being "a half-breed Indian of the United States," he wrote in his resignation, he was "regarded by the people as favoring the Indians more than he should do, and hence there is much complaint against him."

It was time to travel again. He looked back on his forty-odd years, lived alternately in two worlds. It had been useful to learn the white man's ways, it helped in dealing with them. But the best times of his life were spent as an Indian or frontiersman in the free reaches of mountain and plain. There was something sinister about the white man's confining cities and businesses, a world of corruption, deceit, intrigue, of prejudice against Indians one could never escape. A few whites he had known, like Prince Paul and notably William Clark, had some feeling for Indian problems, but such men were pitifully few. Yes, Baptiste decided, it was time to go.

His resignation was written in July, 1848. News of the gold discoveries in the Sacramento Valley was spreading over California by then, and in December Baptiste rode north to see the diggings. He tried his luck for a few months—a mountain man he had known years before reported seeing Baptiste panning gold at Murderer's Bar on the middle fork of the American River—but very soon the mines were overrun with lawless, greedy men. There were Europeans as well as Chinese, Mexicans, Indians, Kanakas, but mostly men from the United States pushing the others out in their lust for gold. He watched the

[45]

Americans set up their corrupt government in California and settle like a shroud over that once calm and peaceful land. "Manifest Destiny" they called their takeover; a newspaper back east had coined the phrase.

So this was Manifest Destiny! This was the inevitable outcome, the end of the chosen people's march westward. For the last time, Baptiste Charbonneau turned away from the white man's world. He crossed the Sierra Madre and went down into the desert basin, to the lake of salt and up again, up into the Shining Mountains, to his mother's people.

When the old man died in 1885 there were many mourners to bury him. He had kept a store like a white trader's on the reservation—the Wind River Shoshoni Reservation in Wyoming—but to the end he lived in a skin tepee. He had had two Shoshoni wives who gave him two sons and a daughter; before he died there were many grandchildren, all being brought up, as much as reservation life allowed, in the proper Shoshoni way. He was known and loved throughout the reservation, and he had white friends there too.

He had grown heavy in his last years and looked more so because of his short stature, only five feet six. He always dressed as an Indian, in buckskin clothes and moccasins, and wore his hair in braids. Until his last illness he was a very hearty old man. Every day, summer and winter, he went to bathe in the Wind River, even when he had to break the ice.

The mourners carried the body from his tepee into the mountains seven miles west of the Shoshoni agency. In

Shoshoni camp on the Wind River Reservation at the time of Charbonneau's death.

those years they had found a way of keeping white settlers from rifling Indian graves: the body was lowered with ropes forty feet into a crevasse where even wolves could not get at it and stones were dropped into the abyss until it was covered. In later years avalanches hid the site.

✵ *In 1910 Quanah Parker, the aged last chief of the Comanches, persuaded the federal government to grant permission and money to have his mother's remains taken from a Texas village graveyard and reinterred, in an elaborate ceremony, in a mission cemetery on the Comanche reservation in Oklahoma. Quanah died the next year and was laid to rest beside her. With these burials many ghosts were laid.*

Seventy-five years before, the Comanches had taken Quanah's mother to live with them. They were lords of the southern prairies then, the tribe most feared by travelers on the Santa Fe Trail and settlers in the country to the south of that great road. As it became a more frequented highway, with a surge of white men ravaging their hunting grounds, the Comanches retaliated with an endless guerrilla warfare, which continued into the time of Quanah's boyhood. But by then the Comanches were no longer holding out for control of the south plains, they were fighting for their lives.

In the short years of his youth, Quanah suffered great losses. His mother was captured by white soldiers, his father was killed, his younger brother Pecos died in an epidemic of smallpox introduced by whites. Quanah became a chief of the Comanches as his father had been, and fought white men as his father had done.

In 1867, at the great treaty council at Medicine

[48]

Lodge Creek where white soldiers tried to persuade the Indians to settle on reservations, Quanah heard from a white man of his mother's last years and how she had starved herself to death. He also listened well to the council's talk of reservations and annuities for red men, and measured the strength of his people against the power of those winds of change that were blowing across the prairies. A few years later, in 1875, he led his people to a reservation and into a peaceful settlement with white men. The Comanches were the last major tribe to give in to the restrictions of a reservation.

Quanah's mother was a white woman. But a twist of fate made it fitting that after his life of compromise with white men and loss to them, he should, as his last public act, bring her back to the Comanches.

☼ CHAPTER THREE

Preloch's Story

A line of mounted warriors rimmed the horizon, Comanches, Kiowas, Wichitas, their colorful war gear glittering in the spring morning air. Their eyes swept the fields of burgeoning corn and wheat and in the center the cluster of cabins surrounded by a twelve-foot palisade. Besides the twenty-odd women and children they counted eight men in the settlement, one very old.

Was it worth it, Elder John, the long trek of your life,

*from Georgia to Tennessee to Illinois to Texas? When
you saw those heathens watching, were you glad you'd
founded your clan and preached your faith and built your
Parker's Fort in defiance of them, and on their own prairie? And when those Godless Red Devils struck you
down did you die, John Parker, a righteous patriarch as
you had lived?*

It was nine in the morning, the day well started and
every soul at Parker's Fort about his tasks. So fine a day
caused many to sing hymns of praise as they labored,
but one by one, seeing the line of heathen warriors three
hundred yards away, they let the hallelujahs die on their
lips. In the gasping silence it was Brother Ben Parker who
laughed and drawled, "See their white flag? It's on'y food
or 'baccy they're beggin. I'm goin out to see."

*Was it worth it, Granny Parker, bearing and mothering
your sons, loving their children in turn, to see some murdered and others ravished away? Did you grieve, sorrowful mother, to see young Ben cut down with their
feathered lances and Silas butchered trying to close the
gate against them, to see those howling savages carry off
Silas' little John and Cynthia Ann? Did you weep at your
losses then?*

Ben came back saying, "I told 'em they could have a
beef an some flour, but I think they're goin to do sunthin ugly. Y'all git ya rifles loaded." Young Ben, fancying
himself a skilled frontiersman and safe in the hands of the
Parker's Baptist God, went out from the fort again to deal
with the Comanches.

*Was it worth it, Brother Ben, the land you Parkers took
from the Indians? The price you gave in exchange was*

A *modern reconstruction of Parker's Fort on its original site.*

high: your life; your untried virility; the small experience of your youth. 'Mama,' you cried out (Did she hear you, Ben?), 'I didn't go to die this way!' and 'Papa, help me, God, help me!' When you felt the hot thrust of the lance blades in your chest and groin and thighs, did you think it worth that price to be a bold frontiersman then?

Ben was the first to die. His older brother Silas fell next, then their father, Elder John Parker. Two other men were killed while the Indians looted the fort. Granny

[51]

Parker, Elder John's wife, was stabbed but escaped death by pretending to be dead. All the other inhabitants of Parker's Fort escaped by hiding in creek-bottom thickets, except for those taken captive: Cynthia Ann Parker, aged nine, and her six-year-old brother John, their cousin Rachel Plummer with her fifteen-month-old son, and Rachel's aunt Mrs. Elizabeth Kellogg.

The Indians attacked Parker's Fort on May 19, 1836. The captives were recovered within the next year or two, except for Cynthia Ann Parker, who lived for twenty-four years and seven months with the Comanches.

Preloch remembered her fourteenth year for two reasons. The most important was that it was the year she changed from a girl child into a young woman, but also in the autumn white traders came to the camp on the Canadian River, where Preloch's adopted family had gone to visit their relatives in the Kwahadi band of the Comanches. Preloch had lived with the Kwahadis for a time, but had then been adopted by a family of the Penateka band, the Honey Eaters, whose home was southeast along the Brazos River.

She had good reason to remember the traders. She had not seen any whites in a long time and when they came into the camp, two dirty, bearded men with a Delaware Indian guide and half a dozen pack mules, she was with the other boys and girls clustered about them to see what good surprises they would take out of the pack saddles. The headmen of the village greeted them and gave them permission to trade. As the whites unpacked, they laughed and joked loudly, trying through an assumed familiarity to hide their fear of the Comanches. Then one of them noticed Preloch.

"Looky thar, Len," he said, "I b'lieve that's a white girl." Preloch looked down at the ground and backed away from their stares. It was embarrassing to be pointed out in that way—Comanche men and boys did not behave so rudely. She went home and told her mother about it.

Later, when the trading was over, a messenger came from Paha-yuca, chief of the Penateka band. Preloch's foster father, he said, was to bring her to talk with the white traders. Uncertainly, she rose to follow, but her father said to her as they left their tepee, "I will not sell you to them." Filled with thanks and relief, she clutched his hand. Sometimes captive girls were sold as slaves to the Apaches, or to Comancheros, or to unscrupulous white traders. She had been fortunate in being treated always as an adopted daughter, never as a slave.

The two men stood under a tree waiting, smiling and making jokes when the girl and the two stern-faced warriors approached. Preloch sat down, looking modestly at the ground like any well-mannered Comanche girl of fourteen in the presence of adult men. Her father and Paha-yuca stood by but the two white men squatted in the dust, hoping she would look at them as they talked and identify herself as the missing Cynthia Ann Parker.

Although their language had a familiar ring Preloch understood very little of what they said. She had not heard English spoken in more than four years. "I an Colonel Williams hyare wanta ransom this pore chile . . ." began the one who had first noticed her. It was clear they were trying to make some sort of bargain but only a few

[53]

words made sense to her. When they spoke the names "Parker" and "Cynthia Ann" she looked up and they saw her blue eyes, almost the only feature that distinguished her from other Comanche girls. Colonel Williams said, "Think we kin give these boys a coupla mules for the kid, Mr. Stoal?" implying by his tone that he thought it a generous and friendly offer. They chattered on, forcing smiles as they talked. Preloch saw the smiles were masks behind which was an expression she feared but could not know was greed for the rewards they might receive if they took her back to the Texas settlements. Her father and Paha-yuca listened politely and spoke little but finally made it clear to Colonel Williams and Mr. Stoal that they could not take her away with them.

Disgruntled, annoyed, the two men stopped smiling, strode away rudely to their Delaware guide and train of mules and whipped them out of camp, muttering curses as they went. Among their own people they would tell a long wild tale of how they had tried to save the poor little captive girl, who was too scared and beaten down to admit she wanted help, and how they failed only because their lives were threatened by a whole armed camp of savages.

The daily life of the Penateka band was unruffled by white intrusions for a long time after that. Since Preloch was now a young woman, she was given a new dress made of deerskin worked to an exquisite softness and shaded a pale lemon yellow. Both the skirt, made of two skins, and the poncho-blouse, of a single deerskin, were heavily fringed and decorated with elaborate designs in beads that her mother had bought from the traders. Preloch had long since given up playing with a doll, carrying it in a cradle board on her back like a real mother. For more than two years now she and other older girls had been given tasks like bringing in water and wood for their tepees, going out with the women to gather nuts, roots, and wild fruit, learning to cook and make moccasins, dress skins, and put up a tepee. They were in training to be warrior's wives.

Now came the time when young warriors stood nearby to watch her come and go from her tepee or tried to talk to her alone as she went for water or wood. In a few more years she was a mature and charming woman with much to offer as a wife. Among the suitors were warriors from other bands and it was on one of these that Preloch and her parents agreed. He was a young man of the Nokoni band, already admired as a warrior and thought of as a potential war chief. His name was Peta Nocona.

Young men of the Comanches did not ask for the bride directly. Peta Nocona sent a male relative, as was the custom, to offer Preloch's father a choice selection of ponies as a bride gift. The two men talked politely of small things for a while, then the mediator made the offer and left immediately so there would be no embarrassment in case the father refused it. Next day the bride gift of horses was brought to the tepee and Peta Nocona tied his own horse there too. He waited nearby to see if his gifts would be accepted. The horses were driven to Preloch's father's herd and she herself came out to drive Peta Nocona's horse to the herd, as a symbol that she would care for it and for his other property as a good wife should do. By this ceremony the marriage

[55]

was made. Later he took her home to his tepee.

Marriage and domestic life among her husband's people were a complete fulfillment for Preloch. She was honored, for since polygamy was common among the Comanches, many captive girls were taken as secondary wives only to be the first wife's servants. This appears, however, to have been a love match, as Preloch was Peta Nocona's first choice of the whole Comanche tribe, and he is not known to have taken other wives.

The roving life of the Comanches was exciting and colorful. The whole tribe never traveled together, but in bands, some of not more than a hundred or so people, some much larger. The Nokoni band, to which Preloch and Peta Nocona belonged, was one of the smaller ones. They lived mostly in the valley of the Red River, wintering in sheltered canyons of its tributaries, but traveling most of the year, joining other bands from time to time. The men hunted buffalo, went out on war raids against enemy tribes or the encroaching white men, or raided the border settlements, sometimes into Mexico, for horses and mules.

Soon the young couple became a family. Preloch's first child, born in 1845 when she was eighteen, was a son whom they called Quanah, a son who would later take his mother's name and become famous as the last war chief of the Comanches, Quanah Parker. Eventually a second son, Pecos, was born. Preloch's days were full now with domestic work and caring for the two boys, watching them play and learn to ride, telling them the old Comanche stories by the fire at night, stories of how the Comanches got the buffalo from the man who married the buf-

Preloch (Cynthia Ann Parker) with her baby daughter soon after she was recaptured in 1860.

falo wife, of the great flood that cleansed the world and the recreation of men after it, of the blissful place beyond the sun where people go when they die. Sometimes Preloch was confused in her mind because the stories were so like others she had learned long ago in another, nearly forgotten, life.

Throughout these years, the later 1840's, rumors of Cynthia Ann reached the Parker family in Texas. An army officer was reported to have spoken with her in 1846 but was scared off by her guardians when he attempted to buy her. It was said whenever white traders came to the village she would run away and hide. Finally, in 1851, a definite contact was made by her own brother, John Parker, who had also been a Comanche captive.

"Won't you come home?" he said. "Our family wants you."

"My family is here. This is my home. All this." She indicated the tepees and the extent of plains beyond.

"You'd rather stay slaving away for these dirty Indians?"

"Whites are dirtier. And white women in the settlements work harder than I do. I remember the women slaving away, scrubbing, working in the fields at Parker's Fort. For husbands who preached at them and beat them."

"Don't they beat you here?"

"No."

"Do you remember when we were first captured how they kicked and teased us?"

"That was only the children teasing." She pointed to her six-year-old son, Quanah. "When I was his age, adults beat me for singing or picking flowers. They told me that I was a sinner and I would burn in hell."

"But now you're grown up. Come back with me."

"No. I have my husband, my sons. All I love is here."

As the years passed the Comanche bands were concerned more and more with white encroachment on Comanchería, their vast domain of the southern Plains. Once the Mexican War came to an end their lands were spotted with garrisoned forts and white settlements, and crossed by trails with their heavy traffic of wagon trains, the great white-hooded wagons of emigrants moving westward. Warriors never knew when they might stumble across a train or a troop of blue-coat soldiers and have to defend themselves, for the fearful whites shot first, always assuming Comanches were unfriendly. The white man's frontier pushed slowly west across Comanchería.

In the 1850's the Comanches warred less frequently with enemy tribes, but defensive, retaliatory skirmishes with the whites increased. Peta Nocona gained his fame as a skilled and brave war chief in those years, leading raids against the whites. In 1858 he led war parties against white soldiers in a series of battles by which they penetrated to the very heart of Comanche territory on the upper Red River. Typical of these battles was the one at Rush Springs, in southeastern Oklahoma, in which four hundred troopers attacked a village of Comanches who were traveling to nearby Fort Arbuckle to discuss peace with the military. Fifty-six warriors were killed, 120 tepees burned, over 300 ponies taken. In retaliation Comanche warriors under Peta Nocona and other leaders raided white ranches and settlements, mostly in Texas, for the next couple of years.

During a peaceful interval late in 1860, Peta Nocona and his two sons Quanah and Pecos rode west to the Staked Plains to find a site for a winter village that would be safe from white attacks. Preloch had recently become a mother again, this time with a baby girl; she and the baby were left with the women of the Nokoni band at a camp on Pease River in the Texas Panhandle.

[59]

On the gray morning of December 18th, with a bitter north wind blowing up a sand storm, the band packed to leave the Pease River camp, hoping to join Peta Nocona and settle in the new village before winter storms began. They did not know that a vengeful army of whites had just discovered their whereabouts. It was a ragtag-and-bobtail army composed of sixty Texas Rangers, an army sergeant with twenty mounted dragoons, and a passel of vigilantes from north Texas towns, plus a string of mules loaded with whiskey and other necessaries. The commanding officer of this mixed lot, who had been commissioned a captain for the occasion, was L.S. Ross, in later years a governor of Texas. There was murder in the eye of every man among them; they were, it was announced, "determined to attempt to curb the insolence of these implacable enemies of Texas."

Straggling over the hills in the direction of the Comanche village, the army had found signs of their prey late in the day on December 17th—countless tracks of women and children who had been gathering hackberries, nearby the pelt of a recently killed skunk—and set up a hushed and fireless camp in the bitter cold. In the early morning of the 18th, Ross later wrote, he led them about a mile farther to the top of a hill and "to my inexpressible surprise, found myself within 200 yards of a Comanche village, located on a small stream winding around the base of the hill . . . . my presence was unobserved and the surprise complete. By signaling my men as I stood concealed, they reached me without being discovered by the Indians, who were busy packing up preparatory to a move. By this time the Indians mounted and moved off

A Comanche camp like those Preloch knew as a girl.

north across the level plain." The confusion of breaking camp was compounded by the sandstorm. But even under those circumstances it should have been clearly evident to Ross that what he saw was not a real village but a hunting camp occupied solely by women with children and their servants, a few captive Mexican men. The most casual observer would have known that these men, most of them unarmed, were not warriors. They did not even wear Indian clothes.

The Comanche women were hopelessly trapped. Ross described it thus: " . . . the sergeant and his twenty men were sent at a gallop, behind a chain of sand hills, to encompass them in and cut off their retreat, while with forty men I charged. The attack was so sudden that a considerable number were killed before they could pre-

[61]

pare for defense. They fled precipitately right into the presence of the sergeant and his men. Here they met with a warm reception, and finding themselves completely encompassed, every one fled his own way, and was hotly pursued and hard pressed."

Ross and a friend were the hot pursuers of a group consisting of a man, one of the Comanches' Mexican servants, with a girl mounted behind him, and on another horse a woman carrying a baby. This second woman was captured rather than shot by Ross's friend because, to his surprise and puzzlement, she held up the baby and shouted, "Americano! Americano!" Ross had dashed ahead and shot the younger woman in the back, causing her to fall and drag the Mexican man off their horse. The man immediately began shooting arrows at Ross and when one of them nicked the captain's horse, causing it to buck, he emptied his pistol in the Indian's direction. One shot broke the man's right arm at the elbow and disabled him. At this point the rest of the party came up to them, including Ross's body servant, a young Mexican boy who carried an old Yauger shotgun.

"Shoot 'im!" Ross bellowed. "Shoot 'im 'fore he does sunthin else!"

The Mexican boy gave the man a load of buckshot in the groin, and he sank in agony to the ground. One of the Texas Rangers finished him off with a blow of his rifle butt to the head. Then taking out a knife, an observer recorded, the Ranger "made a quick incision around his head from ear to ear and when he jerked off his scalp it popped like a rifle."

Ross's attention was drawn to his friend, swearing lustily at having winded his favorite horse in chasing the squaw with the baby. Ross glanced at the woman curiously. It was Preloch.

"Why, Tom," he said, "this is a white woman. Injins don't have blue eyes."

Like all Texans of his time, Ross had been brought up on horror stories of Indian raids and captivities, one of the most popular being that of the attack on Parker's Fort and the captivity of Cynthia Ann Parker. He apparently suspected the identity of his captive even then, but made no attempt to establish it, indeed was unable even to question her since she spoke no English at all and none of his men knew more than a few Comanche words. Preloch was hardly in a communicative mood, in any case, seeing her friends and relatives, men, women, and children lying dead all about her. The men expressed concern about her continual weeping as they led her away through the wreckage. "We rode right over her dead companions," one of them wrote.

Preloch was taken under guard to Camp Cooper (in what is now Throckmorton County) where she was held until a message could reach her uncle, Isaac Parker of Weatherford, Texas, the nearest available member of the family. An interpreter was found and Uncle Isaac attempted to communicate with her. Preloch was shy and frightened, appearing to him sullen and indifferent. Frustrated, refusing to believe this creature could be his own flesh and blood, he brought the interview to an end and rose to go. Chatting with Captain Ross, who had come to watch, Parker expressed doubt that she was his brother's daughter Cynthia Ann.

[63]

At the mention of the name she looked up, smiling at them pathetically, perhaps with a bleak, vague hope that the use of name-medicine, very strong among her own people, might release her from her imprisonment. She patted her chest and said, "Cynthia Ann! Cynthia Ann!" Over and over again, her voice urgent, her eyes glistening with tears, "Cynthia Ann . . ."

Cynthi'Ann jes cried for the longest, the Parkers would say.

Course livin with them Injuns s'long—oughtn't to say ugly things about her, but it uz true—she wa'n't quite right in the head. . . .

An we all done so much for her.

Tried to anyway . . . .

An she jes cried an took on, wouldn't even try to b'have like a white woman.

Never tried to talk English at all . . . .

Did you weep, Preloch, that you could not relearn their tongue and tell them what they wanted to hear? Were your tears in sympathy with their frustration when they found you could not say Thank you, sirs, for saving me from my terrible fate?

I wept not to see my husband again, not to see my sons. I wept at our blood on the ground, our tepees burning.

Seems like she could of stayed on at Uncle Isaac's, her sister said, but he kept sayin she oughta be with closer kinfolks. Well, we brought her here to our place, but she'd take her baby an run off ever chance she'd get. An then the soldiers bringin her back, well I jes wouldn't have it. An when the baby got sick an died, I swan I couldn't do

[64]

a thing with her . . . .

Did you grieve, sorrowing mother, at the shortness of her life, at the tiny fragile prettiness lost to party dresses and ranchers' sons?

I grieved that she would not ride the prairies as I had done, and grow to be a warrior's wife and have sons like mine. It was not the dying grieved me: we were captives four years then. Captivity was death to us.

Funny how she seem to jes pine away, her brother said. We give her everything she coulda wanted. Why, I clothed an fed her an she had that pension from the state besides, a hunnerd dollars a year. It uz like she jes give up the ghost, wouldn't talk, didn't care about a thing. Well, Cynthi'Ann passed away in sixty four an we buried her, so I guess she's at rest an peace now. Later sometimes we'd hear about them two boys she had, half-breeds livin wild with the Comanches . . . .

Pecos, killed by the white man's smallpox before he was old enough to be killed by white men's bullets.

Quanah, the war chief who made peace between his Comanches and the whites, and brought Preloch his mother back to her own people at last.

✳ *Furs and gold were the more glamorous attractions to prospective settlers in the west. But ultimately it was land that drew greater numbers of people, land they found to be a richer prize. Fabulous stories were told of the richness of western land, and in some part they were true. Crops that seemed incredible to eastern farmers were produced, particularly in farms carved out of the northwestern forests.*

The United States brought on the Texas rebellion in 1836 and the Mexican War of 1848 and nearly fought a third war with England over the Oregon country, all for the purpose of acquiring vast tracts of land for Americans to settle on. These larger battles mostly ignored the presence of those who had lived on the land before the white men came.

The territory that was to be the states of Oregon and Washington caught the flood tide of land-hungry emigrants in the 1840's and 1850's. Within a single generation, the small, peaceful tribes around Puget Sound found themselves dispossessed and with no compensation for their losses. Muckleshoots, Nisquallys, Puyallups, and others turned into warring tribes and struck back, and theirs was part of a greater rebellion that would involve all the northwest tribes and go on for three years. One of the bloodiest acts of retaliation was the destruction of a string of farms along the White River, near the village of Seattle, in the fall of 1855.

At the End of the Oregon Trail

" . . . the murdering of my mother and stepfather by the Indians . . . made such an impression upon my mind that I was terror-stricken at the thought of another massacre, and the details are indelibly and most vividly fixed in my mind . . . ."

Doctor King tried to brush aside the memories of the ordeal—the fire, the blood, the fearful hiding in the forest—so he could write with a clear mind of his experience, from beginning to end and without the emotionalism that could so easily have colored his story.

"Though a child—"

He laid down his pen. A child of six. Doctor King tried to separate himself from the child he had been, tried to put before his mind's eye the round-faced, brown-haired little boy, his baby fat gone, his awkward years still to come. A manly and forthright boy he saw, but the smile of a Prairie Puck lingered about the eyes and the petulant set of the boy mouth, even after the adventure of the massacre at White River. Half a lifetime before he had been that child of six whose adventure was one no other six-year-old had experienced and lived to write about forty years later. The doctor made an effort of will to control the still painful memories "indelibly and most vividly fixed in my mind," as he had already written, and began at the beginning.

[67]

"I was born in Harrison township, Grant county, Wisconsin, November 13, 1848. When I was five months old my father started for the gold diggings in California, but died shortly after reaching that state. In the early part of 1851 my mother married Harvey Jones. In the spring of 1854 we started for Washington territory, overland, reaching our destination on White river in the fall, having been six months and five days in making the trip...."

Across the prairies they rolled through Wisconsin and Iowa, crossing the wide Missouri into Nebraska and on to the river Platte, the white covered wagons, which seemed so immense to young Johnny, like a string of pearls on the vast spring-green cushion of the rolling grassland. Like many emigrant families, they did not travel the whole length of the Oregon Trail but joined it somewhere along the Platte. And like most, they were lured by extraordinary tales of the northwest country— Oregon and the newly created Washington Territory— lands of milk and honey, free of the prairies' summer heat, winter frosts, and howling winds, lands free for the asking and so unbelievably rich as to yield two or three fabulous crops a year, wheat six feet high with seven kernels on each stalk, oats taller than a man, turnips and beets three or four feet around.

Once well out on the trail, they began to think that the new country would have to be as spectacular as the tales described it to make up for the pains of the trip. John remembered how the sparkling spring days turned to withering summer heat as they approached the mountains. Travel became a grueling routine of sour-tasting water, monotonous food, and the constant plodding

[68]

Johnny King (standing at right) with Edith and Edward, and (above) with his mother.

onward to the mountains. They were all sick from time to time; Johnny's mother seemed always to be cross, the two babies fretful. He was old enough to understand that they were often in danger from Indian attacks, but none occurred, so his curiosity about Indians was not satisfied. But occasionally there were startling landmarks, and the country changed—Chimney Rock and Scotts Bluff, then finally Independence Rock, through South Pass to Bridger's Fort and the cruel mountain crossing.

When they were across the worst of the mountains and into Washington at last they met some people who had already pioneered their farm settlements on the shore of Puget Sound. They were directed to specific choice locations southeast of a blockhouse and village that was beginning to be called Seattle.

"My stepfather took up land on White River some twenty miles up the stream from Seattle," Doctor King wrote. "At that time there were only five or six families in the settlement, the nearest neighbor to us being about a fourth of a mile distant."

The extravagant stories about the country were somewhat overdrawn, but they had expected that. Still it was grand and lovely, green the year round, the great forests almost untouched by man. Johnny's stepfather cleared a swale in the woods for their cabin, which he built from the quantities of timber he cut down. Before Christmas, 1854, they were well settled, and in the spring neighbors helped them put up a substantial new three-room house. The log shack, their original shelter, was then a barn and quarters for Enos Cooper, the hired man who helped with farm chores.

The White River near the farm where Johnny King lived.

While Cooper and Johnny's stepfather, Harvey Jones, plowed and planted, the boy with his half sister Edith, almost four, and his half brother Edward, two years old, explored the clearing and its fringes of forest. Even in winter, although constantly rainy, it was never too cold to play outdoors. They never went far into the forest— perhaps its majestic bigness was too awe-inspiring. Sometimes they saw shy black bears shambling away at a human's approach, and sometimes at night the eerie scream of a cougar made them glad for the security of their sturdy new cabin.

There were children on the other farms of the settlement, but for the most part they were, like Johnny King and his brother and sister, too young to run back and forth the considerable distances through the woods from

[71]

one farm to another. In any case, the visitors who fascinated Johnny, Edith, and Edward most were the Indians.

These were talkative and friendly people of the Muckleshoot, Klickitat, and other local tribes. They seemed to like the children and would tell them long Indian tales and teach them words in Chinook jargon, the pidgin English of the northwest. Their tribes, they said, were *tillicum*, the original people of *illahee*, that forest country called Oregon by the *Bostons*, or white men (so-called because the first whites they knew had come in ships from Boston). The Indians encouraged the children of the *Bostons* to call them "our *tillicum*," for they wanted to be brothers of the whites. The first *Bostons* had also told them they were savages, a word they did not understand and which came out on their tongues *siwash*.

Johnny soon missed many of these pleasant visits because he was sent to a school established by a Mr. Thomas in his farmhouse two and a half miles up the river from the Jones's farm. Mr. Thomas kept school through the summer but when harvest time came in early fall he dismissed his classes.

The settlement on White River appeared to be well established by that autumn of 1855. Farms were thriving, new settlers came to open up more land, they had a school and occasional social events like a house-raising, which would include a picnic and square dance. The not-too-distant town of Seattle grew every day with more homes, warehouses, mills, and stores.

The only blot on this pleasant picture of prosperity was a rumor: the Indians all over Washington Territory were in an ugly mood. Their land was being rapidly taken from them by the *Bostons*, and the settlers on White River heard of more and more incidents of retaliation against whites.

"Some of the settlers became alarmed," Doctor John King remembered, "at reports of hostile intentions by the Indians upon our settlement and left some two weeks before the outbreak. Among those who thought their fears groundless and remained was our family."

Harvey Jones and his wife could not believe that those mild-mannered, cheerful people would become hostile. Mrs. Jones in particular was used to seeing small groups pass the house and greet her and the children. Often they would come from a fishing trip to the Sound and offer her a fine cod or salmon "from *salt-chuck*" they said, by which they meant the sea. Then, "*Supalel?*" they would say, hoping she might pay them with one of her fresh-baked loaves of bread: "*Bostons lady supalel?*" They found her baked goods the most luxurious treats imaginable.

Some of these Indians the Jones family had come to know rather well, particularly a man the children called Tom, who hired out for occasional work on the farms, and an older man whom the whites called Chief Nelson. Tom lived on the river nearby, spoke pretty good English, and was liked and trusted by all the settlers. Nelson, on the other hand, they regarded as a pleasant and amusing nuisance. He visited the farmhouses frequently. The children grew extremely fond of him because he would tell them fascinating myth-stories of ancient days in that *illahee* when it was occupied by strong, fierce, giant Indians who still haunted the forests at night as ghosts, or

[73]

statalth, hugely tall specters that chased people out of the dark woods. Many a delicious shiver ran down Johnny King's spine as he listened to Nelson's tales, but the old Indian's funny broken English kept them from being too frightening.

By late summer of 1855, Chief Nelson was coming to the Jones's house two or three times a week. He seemed to regard them as particular friends. Obviously he enjoyed being with the children and liked to talk to their mother, who had learned Chinook jargon. Nelson would sit in her kitchen, tell the children stories, and chat with her while she cooked and cleaned, hoping of course to be treated to a crisp-crusted roll or loaf of bread.

Suddenly, in early October, Nelson's visits stopped. Just as suddenly, two weeks later, he appeared again, but when Mrs. Jones opened the door to his familiar guttural greeting (he never knocked) Nelson seemed aloof and distant. He stayed only a short time and spoke hardly at all. The next day he came again, and the next, but spoke even less. When he was leaving the last time, however, he turned a solemn countenance to Mrs. Jones and said:

"Soon all Siwash be gone, Bostons have all land, all land here!"

It was sternly spoken, like a warning, but the statement made no sense to Mrs. Jones. Neither could her husband or Enos Cooper make anything of it. The following Sunday they were made forcibly to understand that it had been an expression of long-suppressed resentment against the whites who had taken all the Indians' lands.

"On Sunday morning, October 28, 1855, while at breakfast," Doctor King wrote, "we were surprised, and the

[74]

house . . . surrounded by a band of hostile Indians, who came running from the grass and bushes, whooping and discharging firearms. They seemed to rise from the ground so sudden and stealthy had been the attack . . . ."

Johnny's mother had risen from the breakfast table to open the door at the familiar sound of a grunted greeting. Everyone assumed it was Chief Nelson. But as she opened the door a strange Indian standing by the log barn fired his musket at the house. She slammed and bolted the door. The first shot touched off a barrage of firing. Through a window Johnny could see Indians swarming into the clearing.

"As soon as the Indians began firing into the house," the Doctor remembered, "my mother covered us children over with a feather bed in the corner of one of the rooms farthest from the side attacked."

Enos Cooper returned some shots while Mrs. Jones hid the children and got her husband's weapon, a five-shooter. Jones himself was in bed, sick with pleurisy. The two younger children, Edith and Edward, whimpered for their mother, but Johnny was excited by the sudden explosion of rifle fire and much too curious to stay hidden under the feather mattress. He couldn't resist putting his head out from time to time to see what was going on. Even to a six-year-old it was clearly a desperate situation.

"In a short time it became evident we were entirely at the mercy of the savages. . . ."

Johnny observed a hasty conference between his mother and Mr. Cooper; then the hired man broke out of the cabin through a back window, apparently in an attempt to go find help for the besieged family: " . . . he came into the room where I was, and with an ax pried off the casing of the window and removed the lower sash, and then jumped out, but as was afterward learned he was shot when only a few rods from the house."

Harvey Jones by this time had struggled out of bed and was coming into the kitchen to aid his wife. As he passed through the doorway a wild shot sang through the window and caught him in the chest. He collapsed immediately. Soon the shooting stopped, since there was no more resistance from the house. Johnny, poking his head out to see why it was quiet, realized the Indians were in the house. He saw one carrying out his mother's breadbox full of loaves.

Johnny, Edith, and Edward tried to keep quiet, but three small children half smothered under a feather ticking cannot stay still for long.

"Soon we were taken out by them. I did not see my mother. We were placed in the charge of the leader of the band who directed them in their actions. They put bedclothes and other combustibles under the house and set fire to them, and in this way burned the house. When it was well nigh burned to the ground, we were led away by one of the tribe, who in a short time allowed us to go where we pleased."

The leader of the band was Chief Nelson. He sat as if enthroned on an upended section of a log, directing the activities of his tribesmen. Johnny King was too astonished to be frightened, so indignant that his own friend Nelson was supervising the destruction of his home that he could not cry. The two younger children were paralyzed with fright. It occurred to Johnny that his step-father was in the house and would be burned, but Chief Nelson refused to hear his protest or speak to him. There was an aloof and menacing air about him now. The sight of the fire held them all hypnotically until the flames began to go down, then Nelson instructed a young Indian to lead the children away and lose them in the woods. The young brave grumbled and unwillingly led them a short distance out of the swale, but soon left them and hurried back to his companions.

Johnny's first thought was to find other white people. For the first time he was beginning to feel fear. He pushed Edith and Edward into a thicket and gave them stern orders to stay there quietly until he came back. Then he ran a quarter mile to the nearest house. It was midday by then and he was confused to find the door open and the house ransacked, but no one present. He did not know the Indians had stopped there before coming to attack his parents' farm. He ran all the way back to the burned remains of his own home, forgetting for the moment to look for Edith and Edward in the thicket.

Bursting into the clearing, Johnny saw that the Indians were gone. But prowling in a half-daze around the smoking ruins of the house, he came suddenly upon his mother. She was lying on the ground, conscious but unable to move. With a sob, he sank down beside her.

"Johnny," she said, "I can't leave, but you can save the children. Take them to the Thomases'." Her voice was low and tense; Johnny knew she was hurt and could say no more. He wanted to object, but her near-panic communicated to him. He remembered suddenly he had left the children somewhere in the woods. He hugged his mother and ran off past the burned house, stopping only to pick up some potatoes that had been roasted in the fire. His expense of energy, both physical and emotional, had made him ravenously hungry.

Finding Edith and Edward, Johnny fed them each a roasted potato as he urged them along the trail to the Thomas farm. A few weeks before Mr. Thomas had been schoolmaster and his farm kitchen the classroom, so Johnny knew the trail to it well. But now it was not so easy a path to follow: there was the fear that some of the Indians might be lurking in the woods—he was afraid of them now—and he had to pull Edith along by the hand and carry little Edward. It was two and a half miles through thick forest. To Johnny it seemed hours later when they finally arrived.

The Thomases' door was locked, the house deserted. Immediately Johnny hurried the children on to the next farm, another mile. It too was abandoned, and it was the farthest outpost of the settlement. There was no place farther to go, so he went back to Thomas' farm. His arms ached with Edward's weight but he kept moving, wandering aimlessly along the trail. The daylight was beginning to fade. Edith whimpered and stumbled and little Edward began to fret and cry for his mother.

"Stop it!" Johnny said. "You stop it now or the Indians'll kill you."

It was an effective threat. Both Edith and Edward were silent as Johnny settled them in a small hollow a few yards off the trail. He tried to think what to do next. Off in the distance soft footfalls whispered along the trail. He sat dully, wishing for help, fearing whatever approached might be a threat. He left the younger children and moved closer to the trail to see.

Dusk was settling over the forest. Johnny strained his eyes to see a tall, shadowy figure approaching. In the half light it seemed to float along the trail. He shivered and thought: *Statalth*. It was just as in the stories Chief Nelson told. He could not move or cry out. The children had always been warned not to stay in the woods after dusk, and now he had brought them here, it was his fault the pickle they were in. He sat waiting, hopelessly, until the figure was only a few feet away. Then a flash of recognition struck him.

"Tom!" he screamed. He leaped onto the trail and threw his arms around the man—for it was, after all, a man. It was Tom, the Indian who lived on the riverside near them and worked for the *Bostons* on their farms. He was startled to be so suddenly confronted with a hysterical small boy bursting forth from what only a moment before had been a silent and deserted forest. But Tom knew about the Indian attacks on the local farms and soon grasped the situation. In no time at all he had calmed Johnny's fears, collected the two smaller children, and shepherded them the rest of the short distance to his lodge by the river.

Tom's squaw received them with open arms, but was puzzled at Edith's and Edward's behavior. They cried and backed away whenever she tried to come near them and they would not eat the meal she prepared. They were afraid of all Indians now, particularly after Johnny's warning in the dark woods. He, however, hungrily ate dried salmon and a bowl of serviceberries. Then she spread a thick-furred bearskin on the floor for them and the children lay down.

"I take you Seattle," Tom said to Johnny, "when moon is high." He pointed to the smokehole in the center of the lodge's roof.

Johnny woke from his exhausted sleep at the sound of Tom's canoe being dragged into the river. He looked up and saw the moon through the smokehole. Then Tom was waking the other children and soon all three were settled in the bottom of the canoe, gliding through moonlight down the calm stretch of White River. The whole adventure had taken on a dreamlike unreality for Johnny, like one of Nelson's stories. At daybreak they were in the Sound. Seattle could be seen sleeping on the shore, but nearer than Seattle was a warship of the United States Navy, the *Decatur*, lying at anchor, and the children were delivered there.

It was over. They were safe. An uncle was contacted in California and he came for them in the early spring of 1856. Johnny and his brother and sister were the only survivors of the massacre on the banks of White River.

Doctor John King, the respectable, middle-aged, successful physician of Burgh Hill, Ohio, looked over the manuscript he had written. Those wild times were a world away. He looked back at them through a perspective of his later boyhood in Ohio, being brought up by his mother's relatives, studying medicine, setting up his practice. Well, it wouldn't do to dwell on those old adventures. He took up his pen again and concluded briskly:

" . . . We went to San Francisco and then to the Isthmus,

[80]

and from there we went to New York City. From there we were taken to Wisconsin, where my brother and sister remained. I was brought back to Ohio in September, 1856. They both died in October, 1864, of diphtheria, in Wisconsin.

"John I. King, M.D."

☼ *The greatest thrust of the westward movement came after the discovery of gold in California. In the years from 1849 to the beginning of the Civil War every trail was crowded and new paths to California were sought out. One of these was the old Gila Trail across New Mexico Territory and part of northern Mexico. It took gold-greedy emigrants through an exotic and fearful land, a country of the extremest contrasts. Raw desert punctuated only with ragged mountains gave way surprisingly to pine forest and highland lake, or in some of its flattest, driest stretches to a ribbon of water such as the Gila or the Colorado. The natives of this land were equally extreme. Papagos and Mohaves, placid, easygoing tribes, were the neighbors of fiercer people, Apaches, Yavapais, and Navahos.*

White travelers, having run the terrifying gauntlet of Apachería, with its harsh dry hills and gullies, sometimes gained a false sense of security by next coming in contact with Papagos or the Pimas with their pleasant Gila River farms. California seemed so near . . . . The travelers hurried on, not knowing they still had the worst of the desert to cross, part of it occupied by tribes as savage as the Yavapais.

CHAPTER FIVE

Search for the Tattooed Girl

Lorenzo stood disheartened and bitter at the edge of the Fort Yuma parade ground, watching the garrison muster for their departure. The company's bugler sounded the order to mount and the double line of soldiers rode out past him. It was difficult for the fourteen-year-old boy to understand why Major Heintzelman, the commanding officer at Yuma, could not have sent at least a few of all these soldiers back into the Arizona desert to search for his two sisters, captives of the Yavapais.

"What do you expect me to do, boy?" the Major had said. "Leave this post half-garrisoned and send men wandering all over the territory looking for those savages? Why, I'd be as much a mad fool as your father was coming out across that desert alone with a family. I'm sorry they've been killed and the girls taken, but you'd better face up to it—your sisters aren't likely to be alive either by now. Those Indians don't take the kindest care of their captives."

Lorenzo's father, Royse Oatman, had been confident he could go safely ahead of the settlers' train he was traveling with and get his family in their single wagon all the way to Fort Yuma without mishap. At the Gila River crossing, Oatman became aware of danger and sent a message to Fort Yuma begging help, and Major Heintzelman had sent a troop of men the eighty miles upriver, only to find the grisly remains of a massacre. The Yavapais had killed the parents and four of their children, left Lorenzo for dead, and carried off his sisters Olive and Mary Ann.

Six weeks later, Lorenzo, recovered from his wounds and the shock of losing his family, could not be convinced that Olive and Mary Ann were dead. He had seen the Indians take the girls aside when they attacked, and their bodies were not found with the others later. Mary Ann was always frail, sick with what his mother called the consumption, but Olive was a strong thirteen-year-old girl who would take good care of her little sister. Lorenzo was particularly attached to Olive, and determined to find her.

His family had been attacked on March 18, 1851. Now it was May and the Fort Yuma troops were ordered to San Diego, leaving only a dozen men to guard the ferry that crossed the Colorado River at that point. Emigrants, including the group the Oatmans had left, crossed on that ferry, but no one would take Lorenzo back to look for his sisters. Everybody wanted to get on to California, some to the gold fields and some to find farm land. They all urged Lorenzo to give up his search and go with them. A strapping teen-age boy would be useful in California; nobody would believe his sisters could ever be found—except Lorenzo.

The boy clambered into the army wagon in which he was to travel with Dr. Hewitt, the post surgeon, who had taken charge of Lorenzo and planned to find him a home and a job. The wagons pulled out behind the mounted troopers who were strung out westward in the hot light of the California desert. It was only late spring but already the men were sweating in the simmering heat. Lorenzo gazed back past the scattered buildings of the little fort and the river to the Arizona desert on the other side. Somewhere in that expanse of cactus, greasewood, and rocky soil the Yavapais were holding Olive and Mary Ann.

Dr. Hewitt noticed his backward glance. "Wouldn't do you any good to stay here, son," he said. "You couldn't find them alone"

"I'd like to try."

"That's a way to commit suicide, Lorenzo. Be sensible. When we get to San Diego, we'll take ship for San Francisco and get you settled there. Maybe in a few years when you're old enough to strike out on your own these parts will be more settled. Then you can come back here, poke around, maybe find a trace of your sisters. Meantime let me look at that scalp wound."

Lorenzo dutifully turned his head so the doctor could examine the spot where he had stitched the skin back together. It was healing nicely. The Yavapai warriors had struck the boy down with their heavy war clubs, then dragged him to one side, assuming they had killed him. That was nearly true, but Lorenzo survived their beating. He finally came to, battered and aching. Every move had been torture but he dragged himself ten miles down the road, where he was found by some friendly Pimas who took him back to their villages. There were camped the other emigrants with whom Lorenzo and his family had traveled from Illinois and they carried him to Fort Yuma, where Dr. Hewitt took over in both a medical and a fatherly way.

The troops pulled into San Diego and Dr. Hewitt was free to leave, as he was retiring from the army. He left for

[85]

San Francisco with Lorenzo Oatman on June 20, 1851. By the end of that summer, a home and a job in a store had been found for the boy, who was biding his time till he could go back to the Colorado River country and look for his sisters.

In the early spring of 1852 a group of Mohave Indians, half a dozen men and a young woman, the daughter of their leader, went from their town on the central Colorado River to visit and trade with their neighbors the Yavapais. They had a few horses, a stock of sea shells and beads, and baskets of sun-dried vegetables. These items they offered in exchange for the two white girls the Yavapais had captured a year before.

Olive Oatman was aware that she and her young sister Mary Ann were the subject of the haggling between her masters and the Mohaves, but she was too exhausted to care. For nearly a year they had been slaves of the Yavapais, working from dawn till after dark every day searching for food and firewood, tending fires, and carrying burdens. They were in the charge of cruel and impatient squaws who seemed to be constantly screaming orders at them. Most often the screams were punctuated with the stinging blows of a greasewood switch. There was never enough food. During the winter supplies grew scant; the Yavapais ate little and the two girls went hungry.

The trading talk between the Yavapais and their visitors went on well into the night. Next morning a bargain appeared to have been struck: the Mohave girl with the trading party came to them smiling and gesturing. She made them drop the bundles of sticks they were collecting for the morning fires and led them away to join her kinsmen who were then leaving the Yavapai village. Olive and Mary Ann, dirty, ragged, dumb with fatigue and hunger, followed her like beaten dogs, cringing as the Yavapai squaws and children shouted insults after them.

The party struck out along a desert trail, west with the sun. The Mohave girl, whose name was Topeka, talked with them as they walked. Conversation was possible since the Mohave tongue is very similar to that of the Yavapais, which Olive had learned in her year with them.

Topeka and her father Aspenosay were intensely curious about the girls and their adventures. They had difficulty pronouncing their names, so Olive came to be known and was remembered years afterward in the tribe as Aliutman. It was a day or two before she finally realized what an improvement her new life was to be. The Mohaves were sincerely interested in the girls and conerned about their well-being. They were well fed and the group traveled at a leisurely pace so as not to overtire them.

Olive was distrustful at first, puzzled by the contrast. A year ago the seventeen Yavapai warriors who massacred the Oatman family had dragged her and Mary Ann on just such a cross-country journey as this, but at a frenetic pace. The girls' shoes had been taken away then and their feet were soon lacerated by stones and cactus thorns. They were whipped and teased along until nearly hysterical with fear, pain, and exhaustion. The harshness of their

[87]

treatment on that trail and at the Yavapai village had, in its bitter way, softened the shock of having seen their family murdered.

Nevertheless, Olive remembered it vividly. The night before the massacre Olive's father broke down and wept helplessly. She remembered him sobbing to his wife, "Mother, mother, I know something terrible is going to happen." When they were packing the wagon next day the seventeen warriors had come begging tobacco and food, and her father and his family were struck with superstitious terror to see his prediction come true. The Indians suddenly attacked with their war clubs and beat to death her parents, her older sister Lucy, two smaller sisters, and her twelve-year-old brother Royse, Jr. Of course, having seen him fall, she assumed Lorenzo was dead too. The Indians looted the wagon and then grabbed up her and Mary Ann and hurried away, fearful of being seen by other travelers. From then on, life had turned into a meaningless misery, endless pain of hunger and cold, pain of whippings, the aching pain of constant tiredness. It was difficult to grasp that a change for the better had taken place.

The little procession of Mohaves with the white girls paced on toward the river. Ten times they began walking as the sun rose and made camp as it fell; they averaged fifteen miles a day. Soon after the eleventh sunrise they crossed a ridge and looked down on the brown Colorado ribboning through its narrow floodplain, which was already green with spring growth.

The Mohave town of low, earth-covered lodges, each with its adjoining brush-roofed arbor for summer living,

Mohave Indians building a house like that of Aspenosay.

was parallel to the river but on high ground so as to avoid being flooded when the Colorado rose and overflowed its banks. Tired as she was after the 150-mile walk Olive found the neat lodges a cheering contrast to the squalid huts of the Yavapais. The whole atmosphere of the town was happier: no one shouted ugly words at Olive and Mary Ann, the children did not stone them; the Mohaves came out curiously, greeted the girls, and led them to the house of Aspenosay, who was *kohôta*, or head man, of his band. Topeka and her mother, Aspenosay's wife, explained that they were to live there. They were Aspeno-

Olive pounded mesquite beans in a cottonwood bowl as this present-day Mohave girl is doing.

say's adopted children, not slaves as they had been to the Yavapais.

Relieved and pleased at their improved situation, Olive and Mary Ann fell easily into the pleasant and unharried Mohave way of life. In a few days they were learning how to plant corn, beans, pumpkins, and squash, which the flooding Colorado would water and make grow. They were given their own small garden plot to cultivate. After the planting, the women went on food-gathering jaunts, social affairs rather like the work "bees" the girls remembered among the Illinois farm women. They collected cactus fruit, ottileka roots, and the pods of nutritious sweet beans from mesquite trees. The girls were well cared for and were not pressed to work any harder at the women's tasks than Topeka or other Mohave girls. Topeka and her mother treated them like pets.

One day not long after their arrival, Olive was pounding mesquite beans in a big wooden mortar in the airy shade of the arbor. She noticed Aspenosay and another man approaching the house, then heard Topeka and her mother whispering together, something about "*Hakuich . . . hakuich thompol. . . .*" It seemed to be about a surprise and to have something to do with her and Mary Ann. Olive stopped pounding mesquite beans and searched her growing but still limited Mohave vocabulary. *Hakuich thompol*, she thought. The chin. Marking the chin.

Of course: Aspenosay was bringing a friend who was an expert tattoo maker. She and Mary Ann were to be tattooed.

They knew the Mohaves believed that if a person had no such marks on his face when he died, the judge who looked him over as he came to *Sil'aid*, the land of dead people, would refuse him entrance and send him down to where the desert rats are. Consequently almost all Mohaves had tattoos, men on the thigh, the middle finger and the cheek, women on the arms and both sexes on the chin and the forehead. Aspenosay and his family cared enough for their Aliutman and her little sister to plan for their welfare after death as well as protecting them in the world of the living.

Olive was instructed to lie on her back with her head in the tattoo man's lap. He tilted her chin up and drew the design on her skin with charcoal, then with a sharp-pointed sliver of stone he made dozens of tiny pricks where the skin was marked. He worked slowly. As the blood began to flow he gently rubbed fine willow charcoal into the cuts.

It was very painful at the start, but eventually Olive's lower jaw was so numb it no longer hurt. The skin began to swell, and the tattoo maker bathed it with warm water and massaged more charcoal into the lacerations with the palm of his hand.

For four days they could not chew solid food and so were given the soft meat of roasted young pumpkins. Suntanned and weathered as their skin was, the tattoos came out even more clearly than on a Mohave face, in a strong dark blue pattern. All their neighbors came to admire and congratulate them.

As time passed Olive and Mary Ann became used to the indolent Mohave living customs. The ragged remains of their clothes had long since been exchanged for the simple fringed-bark skirts of Mohave girls, and they had grown accustomed to the largely vegetable diet and to the tasks and patterns of the Indians' daily life. Olive's only worry was Mary Ann, who seemed to be weaker and more often feverish or ill as she grew older, rather than improving in the healthy outdoor life. But at least they no longer had the burden-carrying and whippings to bear, as when they were with the Yavapais. Olive felt the Mohaves had saved their lives. In Mary Ann's case, however, it was only to make her dying easier.

The girls had been with the Mohaves over eighteen months when Mary Ann began visibly to fail. In the southwest, 1853 was a particularly dry year and the Mohaves' crops failed. As the autumn and winter wore on everyone felt the pinch of short rations. There was less and less to feed Mary Ann; a combination of famine and, apparently, tuberculosis killed the eleven-year-old girl. When Topeka and her mother began to prepare the body for cremation, as Mohaves always did, some prompting out of Olive's past made her restrain them. White people, she remembered—and explained to her adopted family—were always put into holes in the ground when they died. The Mohaves shied away at the idea of such an unsanitary practice, but Aspenosay, without a quibble, instructed two young men to help Olive dig a hole and inter the little body in it.

So, Olive believed, her last connection with the white world was gone. She could not know that Lorenzo, in San Francisco, was saving his money and waiting for the time when he could spend it on an expedition in search of her, or that Yuma Indians, close relations and friends of the Mohaves would eventually pass the word along to Fort Yuma that there was a white girl living in a Mohave town upriver.

In the spring of 1854 Olive learned about some Mohave customs that were new and startling to her. It was a good spring, food was plentiful, and the young men who had not yet proven their ability as warriors decided to go downriver and settle a disagreement they had had with the Cocopahs by raiding their settlements. There was a seething excitement in the Mohave villages; no major war party had gone out in the two years Olive had been there. She felt a change of attitude toward her that she could not account for. When the warriors had gone she asked Topeka, who tried to explain. It was not that any of them loved their Aliutman the less, she said, but when the warriors came back, and particularly if some of them had been killed, they might be unfriendly to someone not born a Mohave. In the old days some Indians had killed a captive to go with each warrior lost in battle when he went to *Sil'aid*, the land of the dead.

The Cocopahs lived far away, beyond Fort Yuma at the mouth of the Colorado River. It would be many days before the warriors returned. The villages settled into an unnatural calm to wait, three weeks, four, five.

That same summer, Lorenzo Oatman began the search for his sisters. It was the most discouraging period of his young life.

Lorenzo was then eighteen years old. He had left his job in San Francisco and come south to the little town of Los Angeles. Logically, immigrants who had come over the southern trails to California would stop there and might have heard news, or at least rumors, of two white girl captives among the Arizona Indians.

But Lorenzo had no luck. He tried to talk to every emigrant party arriving in Los Angeles, everyone who had traveled the southern route in recent years. Most people thought he was crazy, and told him so, to look for his sisters three years after their capture by the Indians. He could not be convinced that he might never see Olive and Mary Ann again.

His spirits were given a lift when he got a job with a surveying party that was sent to chart some territory east of San Bernardino. At least it put him closer to the desert country where he thought his sisters might be and in his spare time he could scout around southeastern California and pick up gossip or rumors from the settlers. Surely, he thought, one of these new Californians would eventually have some word of his sisters. Hoping for a clue, he listened avidly to any tale of captivities or Indian attacks on wagon trains. He could give his own hair-raising adventure in exchange.

It was unfortunate that Lorenzo did not go back to Fort Yuma in those days. In 1853 a carpenter named Henry Grinnell had gone to work there as a civilian employee of the army. Grinnell liked the country and was interested in the Indians who lived up and down the river. He began learning the Yuma language; the Yumas, unable to make anything of his name, called him "Carpenter." In chatting with Indians who lived near the fort Grinnell heard an occasional tantalizing story of two white girls—or perhaps only one—living with the Mohaves far away upriver. It was exactly the kind of clue Lorenzo Oatman was looking for.

But Henry Grinnell knew little of the Oatman massacre and had no idea that Lorenzo was searching for his sisters, or that the girl, or girls, with the Mohaves might be Olive and Mary Ann Oatman.

When the war party returned there were feasts in the Mohave settlements. The tension of waiting was suddenly dispelled, an atmosphere of joyful celebration spread through the lodges: not only had all the warriors returned safely but they had brought back some plunder and four Cocopah captives, three girls of fifteen or sixteen and an older young woman.

Olive was relieved at the successful outcome of the

[95]

expedition and as curious as the Mohave women about the Cocopahs. The older girl, whose name was Nowereha, was, it developed, a young mother. Her husband had taken their baby and escaped, thinking Nowereha was close behind him. But the Mohave raiders had caught her and she was violently unhappy about being separated from her family. The Mohaves were sympathetic, but she was a prisoner of war, after all, and must accept her fate. Then suddenly Nowereha vanished. During the victory celebrations—it seemed as if she had hardly had time to tell her story—she slipped away. The villages were searched but the Cocopah woman was nowhere to be found.

A few days later a Yuma Indian walked into the Mohave towns leading Nowereha behind him. She had been caught a hundred and thirty miles downriver. Without food, hiding from every shadow or sound of a human, which was not easy on the much-traveled road, she had got most of the distance by swimming.

Now Olive was to witness a celebration of a different sort. The Mohave men made a large cross of cottonwood logs, strapped Nowereha to it by her wrists and ankles. and set it up. Long thin branches from a thornbush were tied around her head to hold it against the upright. The warriors shot arrows at her; firebrands were tossed at her finally, taken from her funeral pyre which was already blazing. Nowereha died within a couple of hours. When Olive questioned the Mohaves, it was explained to her that a missionary had visited them many years before and taught them of such a punishment. They understood it was one the white people used and were surprised Aliutman did not recognize it.

After Nowereha's death, the life of the Mohave towns settled back into its tenor of indolence, sparked only by the Mohaves' natural curiosity about any small novelty. The warm desert days followed one after another, the same gossip was heard around the fires at night. The only difference was that stories about white people coming into the desert country seemed to be more frequent. Fort Yuma had been regarrisoned in 1855 and some of the officers had wives there, who sweated in their funny tent-like dresses and tried to fan away the breathless desert heat. Olive Oatman realized that she listened more attentively to those parts of the talk. Yet, looking up at the glittering stars and the distant horizons of the desert landscape, white people and their life of clothing, houses, and dishes seemed impossibly far away.

Olive liked the Mohaves. She led a comfortable and easy life with Aspenosay's family and neighbors. As far as she knew she had no living relatives or white friends, and consequently no reason to want to go among white people again. No Mohave man ever at any time pressed his attentions on her, but she was then blossoming into young womanhood and would soon want to become a wife and mother. It was puzzling, therefore, the rumor that came one day, a rumor about a Yuma Indian sent by officers at the fort downriver to take Aliutman away.

Lorenzo Oatman had begun to feel a nagging doubt that his search would ever be successful.

He had written Los Angeles' budding newspaper, the *Star*, which took up his cause and published appeals for news of his sisters. He wrote the governor of California, who politely refused his demand for men and money to make a search but also suggested that Lorenzo write the Indian Department in Washington and beg their assistance. He did so, then in December 1855, not waiting for a reply, he hired five men to go with him and scout through the barren desert of southeastern California toward Fort Yuma. The search party found no traces whatsoever, but when they returned to San Bernardino for supplies Lorenzo was greeted by a Mr. Low, a settler who had befriended him, with good news. Lorenzo was elated. He should never have doubted: his faith in his search had paid off at last.

Mr. Low had met a man called Rowlits at the nearby village of El Monte who had talked with Henry Grinnell, the carpenter of Fort Yuma. Grinnell, Rowlits said, connecting the Oatman massacre story with the Yuma Indians' talk about a white girl the Mohaves had bought from Yavapais, deduced that the girl might be either Olive or Mary Ann Oatman. It was not even a definite report, but it was worth investigating.

Both Mr. Rowlits and Mr. Low warned Lorenzo not to let his hopes go shooting up too high, so Lorenzo sensibly went back to work. He had a job for the winter months chopping wood in the San Gabriel Mountains north of El Monte. By spring he would have saved enough money for another searching expedition, this time to the Mohave country.

But the rest of his search turned out to be unnecessary. On the ninth of March, 1856, his friend Mr. Low galloped into the woodcutters' camp waving a copy of the Los Angeles *Star*.

"Lorenzo! Lorenzo!" he shouted. "It's your sister! They've found Olive Oatman!"

[98]

Olive was safe. Lorenzo was weak with relief and excitement. He scanned the brief details in the *Star's* story. She was at Fort Yuma . . . the commanding officer there hoped to contact her brother . . . .

Low loaned him a horse and left with him the next day for Yuma.

After weeks of coaxing, Henry Grinnell persuaded the young Yuma Francisco to go and ask the Mohaves for Olive Oatman.

Like most whites, Grinnell thought of the Mohaves as warlike and unapproachable, in a category with such ferocious southwestern tribes as the Yavapais, Navahos, and Apaches, and so thought it safer to send Francisco than to go himself. He had talked the commanding officer, Lieutenant Colonel Martin Burke, into giving Francisco a letter for Olive and promising a horse and some trade goods if the Mohaves wanted a ransom for her.

"How long you think you'll be gone, Francisco?" he asked.

"In twenty days I will be back," Francisco said, "when the sun is there." He pointed high in the eastern sky, indicating the mid-morning. Then he grinned. "Maybe this girl come with me."

"She better come," Grinnell said. "You tell them Mohaves we'll git after 'em with soldiers if they don't let her come."

Francisco, with a brother and two cousins for traveling companions, set out northward. It was the eighth of February. Word of his journey traveled ahead of him up the river.

On the twenty-eighth of February, about nine in the

morning, one of Francisco's cousins ran into the fort and gave his message to Grinnell: "They come now, Carpenter, like Francisco told you. He says you send a dress for the girl." Francisco had spent less than seven days reaching the Mohaves, four more in palaver with them, and nine days coming back, arriving, good to his word, on the twentieth day.

Grinnell was pleased. By the time he had borrowed a dress from an officer's wife and found some food for the travelers another hour had passed and as he walked down the slope from the fort to the edge of the Colorado River he could see the party at the ferry landing on the Arizona side. There were several Indian men in brief breech-clouts and two brown-skinned young women wearing only their fringed-bark skirts. The carpenter felt a stab of disappointment: it was impossible to tell whether one was a white girl. Even at that distance he could clearly see the tattoo marks on their chins.

But when he had crossed the river and approached the group, the Indians stepped back from Aliutman. He could see then, despite her tanned skin and glossy dark hair, something about the eyes, the shape of the face, that was Caucasian, not Mohave.

"Olive," he said. He held out a hand and she responded with a nod. He showed her the calico dress and led her to a screen of willow bushes at the water's edge where she could wash off the dust of travel. She washed, threw away her Mohave bark skirt, and put on the calico gown. When she was ready Grinnell took her onto the ferry with Francisco, Topeka (the other young woman he had seen), and a young Mohave man called Tokwa Oa.

[100]

Tokwa Oa, in an interview years later, told of Olive's departure from his people. Francisco's party, he remembered, arrived of an evening in the Mohave settlements; as it would not have been proper etiquette, they did not speak of their errand until the next day in a formal meeting with Aspenosay. The *kohôta* considered their request, then said: "Well, I'd like to raise this girl. We traveled far to buy her. We like her. The whites should visit us and see how well we treat her, then they'll treat us well too. If the officers want to see her, they better come here and talk with me. I'll let them have her."

The next day the Yumas came to him again and explained that the officers had sent them as agents and would not come themselves. But: "Those officers will pester you," they said. "That Carpenter will not stop bothering you about the girl." Then they gave Aspenosay the blankets and beads they had brought for a present and told him the officers would give him a horse. So he gave in. He consented to let her go, and Topeka and Tokwa Oa went along to bring back the horse.

Olive had some difficulty deciphering the note from Colonel Burke. She had had very little book-learning anyhow and had seen no written words in over five years. The note read:

> *Francisco, Yuma Indian, bearer of this, goes to the Mohave nation to obtain a white woman there, named Olivia. It is desirable she should come to this post, or send her reasons why she does not wish to come.*
>
> *Martin Burke, Lieut.-Col., Commanding. Headquarters, Fort Yuma, Cal., 27th January, 1856.*

[101]

The note did not entirely make sense to Olive: apparently she could go or stay as she wished. No threat was implied, yet the Yuma messengers said the whites would never leave the Mohaves alone until she went to them. Aspenosay was sad and all the women were downcast; they did not plead with her to stay but some of them would come to her and say, "I like you much, Ali," indicating they wished she would not go.

Topeka went with her, and Tokwa Oa. Aliutman ought to have a Mohave man along to take care of her, he felt. On the fourth day after Francisco had arrived the party set out.

It took them nine days to reach Fort Yuma. They had crossed the river from time to time, since a better trail was sometimes found on the east and sometimes on the west

Fort Yuma (on the hill, upper right) and the Colorado River; the ferry boat took Olive across from the clump of trees (left center) to the foot of the hill.

bank of the Colorado. Once, at a Yuma village, they were given bundles of tule reeds on which they floated a few miles downstream.

And now Olive Oatman was at Fort Yuma. The officers interviewed her, their wives clucked over her and told her how sorry they were about her tattoo. Everyone in the neighborhood, Indian and white, came to look at her. She was confused by their attentions. Then one day a dark-haired, intense-looking young man galloped into the fort and was brought to her.

Olive had been told her brother Lorenzo was alive and searching for her, but at the time of her recovery no one at Fort Yuma knew how to find him. His sudden arrival, therefore, produced an unexpected and emotional scene of reunion. They had been children when they were separated, now they were adults. Neither knew what to expect of the other.

"Olive!" Lorenzo burst out. Then he saw her tattooed chin. "My god—!"

But it was only a momentary hesitation. They had been too close as children not to recognize each other now, not to feel a spark of shared identity. They fell into each other's arms and wept.

Olive's English was very rusty after five years of disuse and Lorenzo spent the next several days helping her relearn it, hearing the story of her adventures and telling his, helping her give interviews for the press. The story became widely known in eastern states as well as in the west through newspaper reports, and then in an immensely popular but mostly fictional book, and in public lectures Olive gave in later years.

Lorenzo Oatman.

Olive Oatman after her return from the Mohaves.

Olive and Lorenzo did not stay much longer in the west. The land their father had hoped to find a settler's paradise seemed brutal and barren to them. A cousin who had settled in Oregon, on learning their story from newspapers, asked them to live with him, but after a visit they left, in 1858, for the east.

On her lecture tour Olive met the young man she later married. They settled in Sherman, Texas, where she died in 1903 after many calm years. She was active in charity work for orphans. She did not dwell on the massacre of her family or the Yavapais, but when she talked about the Mohaves it was with affection. She had told Tokwa Oa she would do so.

When Lorenzo took her away from Fort Yuma, Tokwa Oa had come running up to their wagon, calling out, "You're going?" in Mohave. Lorenzo, misunderstanding and doubtful of all Indians, grabbed up a whip and threatened the boy.

Olive cried out, "Don't, Lorenzo! He's a good man. He took care of me." She got down from the wagon. Lorenzo, in recompense for his mistake, pulled out a box of crackers from their stores and gave it to the young Mohave. Olive said to Tokwa Oa, "This is the last I'll see of you. But I will tell all about the Mohaves—how I lived with them and their good ways. Good-bye." They shook hands. Tokwa Oa helped her into the wagon. He stood holding his box of crackers and watched the wagon roll away.

✵ *Traveling in a wagon train was uncomfortable at best, and often hazardous. Often a family's whole fortune was invested in the lumbering Conestoga wagon, the oxen or mules or horses to pull it, and tools and equipment to set up a new home in the west. It was hard labor managing the great vehicles and their teams day after day for months on end with little rest. At worst on such a journey, both lives and fortune might be lost in a swollen river or on a treacherous mountain trail. Commoner dangers were boredom, violent Plains storms, bad water on which both stock and people sickened, wagon wheels shrinking in the dry air. Accidents were common: more deaths resulted from shooting accidents than from all the Indian attacks of the migration period.*

Yet Indians were a danger, and the danger travelers feared more than any other. Any encounter with Cheyennes or Arapahoes or Sioux was vividly remembered. The Indians watched silently, their anger smouldering as the endless trains crawled across their hunting grounds and the whites chased away or killed off game herds on which their lives depended. Occasionally they stopped a train and warned the emigrants not to cross their territory. Often with no warning at all they made spectacular lightning attacks in revenge. They drove off cattle and horses if they could, and sometimes—it was the fate most dreaded by whites—they took captives.

CHAPTER SIX

The Ghost of Lizzie Fletcher

Mary Fletcher Cook staggered and crumpled into a chair. Her heart pounded, the blood rushed to her head.

The newspaper she had been reading scattered across the living room floor of her house in Salt Lake City. As she gained control of herself, refusing to faint, Mrs. Cook tried to grasp what she had just read: " . . . strange woman . . . believed to be Lizzie Fletcher, captured by Cheyenne Dog Soldiers as a baby in 1865, when they attacked a wagon train at Rock Creek Crossing, Wyoming, with which the Fletcher family was traveling . . . ."

Lizzie Fletcher! Mrs. Cook's baby sister Lizzie, lost over thirty years ago! Could it be? Could Lizzie still be alive?

Mary Cook was a dignified matron lady, and she had long since determined that she would never dwell on sensational memories. . . . She fought down the vision of horrors she had tried to forget, vivid memories, of the Indians suddenly appearing like painted demons in a nightmare, of the burning wagon, her mother bleeding, falling, screaming as she died: "Mary, take care of Lizzie!" Mrs. Cook winced as she saw again the scowling brown man who jerked Mary and Lizzie up onto his horse with him and rode away from that scene of fire, murder, and fear.

She was determined not to let the horrible flood of memories get the better of her. She reached down for the

Mary Fletcher Cook.

newspaper, searched for the article, forced herself to read it to the end: " . . . the blue-eyed, brown-haired woman apparently speaks no English . . . about 35 years old . . . was visiting Casper, Wyoming, with her husband, John Brokenhorn, an Arapaho of the Wind River Reservation."

Yes. It must be Lizzie.

Mary Cook knew what she had to do. After clipping out the article, she disposed of the newspaper and sat down to write a note to her relatives to explain her sudden leave-taking. Then she tidied the living room, packed a valise, dressed herself for the trip, and took the first train that would get her to Casper, Wyoming—to her little sister Lizzie, whom she had lost to the Indians.

As the train climbed out of the valley of the Great Salt Lake, Mary Fletcher Cook tried to imagine what Lizzie's life had been like, how she had survived thirty years among those Indians, and the thought drew her mind back in time. She allowed herself to reconstruct, for the first time in years, the terrible adventure that had shattered her childhood.

It had happened on a Monday, she remembered. It was July 31st, 1865. The Fletchers' wagon was pulled by horses rather than oxen, so it had been put in the lead. When the train of seventy-five ox-drawn wagons behind them halted to camp early that afternoon, the Fletchers' rig was a few hundred yards in advance of the others. The train was camping at the old Rock Creek Crossing on the Overland Trail in Wyoming. They had come through the well-settled area along the Platte River, had seen many white people on their ranches and farms but no Indians at all.

The next day they would pull out toward the wilder mountain country on their way to California.

Jasper and Mary Limb Fletcher were prosperous English business people who had emigrated to America in the summer of 1861 with their daughter Mary and three sons. They went to live in Illinois, but after little Lizzie's birth there, on August 6, 1863, Mrs. Fletcher's health began to fail and they were encouraged to move westward in search of a healthier place than the prairies of Illinois. Denver seemed the logical choice. The climate was perfect, and Mr. Fletcher thought he could set up a successful merchandising business in that thriving young mountain city.

Jasper Fletcher put his entire fortune into a wagon, livestock, and goods to begin a new business in the west. In May 1865 the family started their trek across the Great Plains. But after a few weeks in Denver they changed their minds and continued to Fort Laramie, where they joined the ox train to insure a safe crossing of the mountains.

And on July 31st they camped at Rock Creek Crossing, careless of dangers they had never imagined. They camped a fatal few hundred yards ahead of the other wagons.

Jasper and the three boys had just unhitched the horses when the Indians appeared. Panic swept the family as the silent, painted braves cut them off from the other wagons. The attack came totally without warning, so suddenly they could not even call out for help to the other travelers. Jasper Fletcher cried out in pain as arrows struck him down. Arrows showered them; a flaming arrow hit the wagon and it burst into a blaze.

Mary, with little Lizzie in her arms, felt the throbbing sting of an arrow's tip in her leg, another in her hip. She jerked them out, trying not to drop the baby. Only the thick folds of her skirt prevented serious wounds. Paralyzing, dry-mouthed fear kept her from feeling pain.

Then a cluster of Indians closed in around the invalid Mrs. Fletcher and her daughters. Mary hugged Lizzie and clutched her mother's hand. Her mother was rigid with terror. Suddenly the Indians, laughing, snorting, grunting to each other, were pulling at them, tearing Mrs. Fletcher away from Mary and the baby. Mary saw her mother pushed to the ground, heard her scream and cry out:

"Mary, take care of Lizzie!"

Mercifully, Mary had not seen the mortal blows dealt her mother. At that point she was pulled onto a horse, still clinging to her screaming baby sister, and carried away from the wagon camp.

The Cheyennes rounded up Jasper Fletcher's horses expertly and quickly. The settlers from the other wagons were already shooting. The braves galloped into the nearby hills and stopped on a high ridge, less than a mile from the wagons, to see what damages they had done.

Mary saw the smoke curl lazily into the clear summer sky from the burning Conestogas in the valley below. Her father's wagon, separated from the others, was burned out, and she could see the people, tiny as toys in the distance, some carrying buckets of water from the creek, others beating out fires in the half-dozen wagons the Indians had succeeded in setting aflame before their hasty departure.

[111]

Then the Cheyenne braves, turning satisfied from the sight of their depredations, set up camp for the night and gave their captives some attention. Mary's mind was filled with vague and childish fears.

Lizzie never stopped wailing. Mary clung desperately to her, too stunned with shock and fear to give her much comfort. She stared fascinated at the tall red men, at their half-nakedness, at the awesome painted masks of their faces. The warriors muttered together in annoyance, then approached her, poked at her and shouted, indicating that she should quiet the baby. Suddenly the man who had carried them on his pony struck out and Mary collapsed to the ground under his blows. She tried instinctively to shield the screaming baby with her own body, fighting at the men as they tore Lizzie out of her grasp. Soon she lost consciousness under their blows.

When Mary regained her senses, she was quickly aware that no baby's cries interrupted the calm night of the prairie. Lizzie had disappeared. Mary heard only the crackling of a fire and the soft mutterings and laughter of the warriors gathered around it. One of them would break out occasionally in a song-chant to which the others lisened attentively. There seemed to be fewer men now, and they paid no attention to her.

She struggled to her feet, clutching her torn cotton dress about her shivering body. "Lizzie?" she called, fighting down her panic. "Lizzie, come to sister!"

Immediately the braves were after her, assuming her sudden move was an attempt to run away. As they dragged her back into the circle of firelight, Mary screamed again and again, "My sister!—where is Lizzie—

where is my little sister?" It never occurred to her the
Indians did not understand her words. She kicked and
struck at them, wild with anger and fear.

The Cheyennes tied her wrists and ankles and left her
huddled on the ground to shiver and sob through the
night.

At daybreak she saw that Lizzie was nowhere in the
camp, and there seemed to be fewer Indians. They took
her to a Cheyenne Village where she was subjected to an
introductory hazing by the squaws and put to work. But
her hopes rose a little when a man spoke to her in broken
English. A half-breed, she assumed, from his English and
because he was slightly fairer than most of the Cheyennes.

"Please," she begged, "tell me where my baby sister is.
What did they do with her?"

"Baby?" the man laughed. "White baby, she cry. Cry,
cry, cry! We kill."

Mary reeled back as if the man had struck her. Lizzie
dead! Then she was the only one of her family left alive.
A sense of hopelessness overcame her: she had failed her
mother by being unable to take care of her little sister
Lizzie. Now she was lost and alone. Everyone in the world
she knew and loved was gone. In time to come she
would remember how she had prayed then, "Merciful
God, let me die and be relieved, let these people kill me,
let me die . . . ."

The months that followed were a hazy nightmare to her.
Mary gave in to the unpleasantnesses she came to expect.
She quickly turned into a drab slavey of the squaws,
whose only kindness was to find her moccasins and a
worn buckskin dress to replace her summer gingham

A Cheyenne woman bringing wood to her tepee in winter, one of the tasks Mary and Lizzie Fletcher had to do.

when it went to tatters. She was a sort of common servant for all of them.

Mary Fletcher was a fourteen-year-old girl, imaginative and alert, but not prepared to cope in an adult way with her situation, to her so bizarre and so horrifying. Nevertheless, she found that small rebellions helped to keep her mind active. For one thing, she refused to learn a single word of the Cheyennes' language: there was a satisfaction in forcing the squaws to shout and gesture to make her understand when they wanted her to bring in firewood or help them cook. Most of her time was spent helping to care for a herd of ponies. She thought often of trying to run away, she thought of trying to kill herself, but the squaws watched her constantly and she was not allowed to have a knife or other weapon.

In all the time she was a captive, Mary Fletcher never saw her sister. Yet she was haunted by the thought of the helpless baby in the hands of the Cheyennes. It took a more shocking thought to still her worrying: she had no reason to doubt the half-breed who had told her Lizzie was dead.

Mary had other worries too. She never knew what it was not to be hungry, since she refused to eat many dishes the Cheyennes liked, and her body was always bruised from beatings by the squaws. As winter came on her suffering increased. She had been a well cared for little girl. Now, half-starved, she was outdoors most of the time laboring in the constant freezing wind and sleet and snow of a Plains winter. No other clothing was given her but the single buckskin dress and a shoddy army blanket taken from a government train, which also had to serve to keep her warm at night if there was not an extra buffalo robe for cover. She wondered at times if Lizzie could have been rescued. Lizzie was a distant, spectral image to her by then.

Occasionally Mary still thought of trying to escape, but escape, she knew, was impossible. The squaws always guarded her. Then finally, in the spring of 1866, when she had given up hope of ever knowing any other life but that of a slave to her captors, the chance of her rescue unexpectedly came.

With the fine spring weather the Cheyennes traveled south over the flower-strewn prairie to a point below the

Arkansas River in southwestern Kansas. There they set up camp to trade with their friends the Arapahoes and Kiowas. One day soon after camp was established, Mary was ordered to stop working outdoors and go into a big council tepee. Soon she heard bustling activity in the camp, horses approaching, wagon wheels squeaking, much conversation. Whoever it was arriving had brought the Cheyennes flour and bacon: food for a feast was brought into the lodge and the squaws directed her to help prepare it. As Mary fried the bread cakes in bacon grease and helped roast buffalo meat and make coffee, she tried to steal a look outside.

With a shock of recognition, Mary stopped her work. A white man stood among the familiar Indians of the village. She pushed past the squaws and ran out so that the man could see her. Their eyes met; he understood the appeal the girl was too frightened to call out to him. The Cheyenne men, angered at her appearance, tried to draw his attention away from her. Then some squaws pulled her back into the tepee. But when the warriors entered the council tepee for their feast, bringing the white man with them, he immediately spoke to Mary in English.

"Tell me how you got here," he said. "They don't know much English, you can talk to me. My name is Charles Hanger. I'm a trader."

Mary told him briefly of her capture and the hardships of her life. "Please, can't you help me?" added the girl, trying to hold back tears. "They beat me near to death and now I think they want to sell me to the Kiowas, and they're worse—"

Charles Hanger nodded, holding a finger to his lips to

silence her. Then he sat down to talk and feast with the Cheyennes. They were embarrassed that the white trader had seen their captive and irritated that he had talked with her. The atmosphere in the tepee grew tenser as Hanger negotiated with them, and Mary was in a state of emotional torture, experiencing real hope for the first time in her eight months of captivity, but resigning herself to the beating she expected if Charles Hanger left the camp without her.

Minutes dragged into hours as the feast and conversation wore on. When the men finally came out of the tepee, the trader found Mary waiting for him nearby. Smiling, he came to her. "The Kiowas won't buy you," he said. "I'll buy you."

"Oh, thank God!" Mary gasped. "And God bless you, Mr. Hanger!"

"You'll have to stay here tonight," he said, "but I've told them to bring you to me in the morning. I'm giving them my whole outfit to pay for you. But they're honorable, you can be sure I'll get you out of here."

Hanger took Mary Fletcher to Fort Larned, Kansas, where the Special Indian Agent, Major E. W. Wynkoop, arranged with some ladies at the fort to care for her. With their help the bedraggled, frightened child came to life and blossomed like a prairie flower into a shy but charming young lady. Her terrible adventure had come to an end . . .

Mary Fletcher Cook hurried to the end of the uglier memories. The train rattled on into Wyoming. There was so much to tell Lizzie, so many good memories too—how the ladies at Fort Larned had made dresses for her, and consoled her about losing her little sister, and how Major Wynkoop took her to Atchison where the Superintendent of Indian Affairs interviewed her and sent her on to some English friends of the Fletchers in Illinois. Mrs. Cook remembered the startled surprise in their faces when they saw her. They had heard the whole Fletcher family was killed in the Indian attack.

But the Fletchers had not all been killed. Mary was alive, and Lizzie had survived after all. And now Mary could tell her how their father and brothers had been rescued, had recovered from their wounds and lived until only a few years ago. She would tell Lizzie about her wedding to William E. Cook when she was sixteen and how they had gone to Salt Lake City to take care of her father. Mrs. Cook's spirits rose: there was so much to talk about with her little sister Lizzie.

But she had forgotten one thing. The woman believed to be Lizzie Fletcher had lived as an Indian for over thirty years, and neither spoke nor understood English.

In Casper, the local authorities persuaded her to hire an interpreter, who took her in a buckboard to the Wind River Reservation. At the village on the reservation, the curious Indians came out to stare at the strange gray-haired lady in her trailing black gown. The anxiety and uncertainty were almost too much for Mrs. Cook. She clasped her hands together to hide their trembling. Her knees were like water. She was angry at her own nervousness, angry that she might appear weak before these people she hated, people who had enslaved her, stolen her baby sister away, murdered her mother. Her hatred gave her strength and she passed them without returning their stares.

The interpreter led her up to the tepee in which Mr. and Mrs. Brokenhorn lived. Mrs. Cook saw the couple standing in front of the lodge, a stocky middle-aged Indian man and next to him a woman in a faded calico mother hubbard with her hair braided in the Indian style. But the woman's hair was light brown, her eyes were blue, and her skin, dark as it was, seemed to be tanned by the sun rather than naturally dark like the other squaws'.

When she saw the woman, Mary Fletcher Cook gasped and her hand flew to her mouth. "Lizzie!" she whispered. Then aloud: "Lizzie? Oh, my little Lizzie, is it you?"

Mrs. Brokenhorn giggled self-consciously and stepped half behind her husband. The interpreter spoke to Brokenhorn, explaining that Mrs. Cook believed Mrs. Brokenhorn to be her sister. Brokenhorn then spoke to his wife and she came forward, studying Mary Cook intently.

She cocked her head to one side and the sun caught a red-gold glint in her brown hair. Then she smiled.

"Oh, Lizzie, my god, it is you!" Mrs. Cook burst out. Her emotion overcame her and she threw her arms around the woman. "That's just how you used to look at me when you were—oh, such a little girl! That same smile!"

Mrs. Brokenhorn, embarrassed and confused, tried to pull back, but Mrs. Cook clung to her hands, saying "Lizzie, don't you know me? It's your big sister Mary. I've come to take you home with me." When the interpreter had translated her words, Mrs. Brokenhorn jerked away and stepped behind her husband.

Mary Cook was at a loss. "Please, sir," she begged the interpreter, "make her understand me. I came to help her, I came to take her away. She's my own sister, I want

[119]

to take her home with me where she belongs—take her away from these Indians!"

The interpreter began telling them what she had said, but Mrs. Cook broke in: "Lizzie, don't you remember the horrible things those Indians did to us? And they told me you were dead—and Lizzie, Papa was alive after all, and the boys too, our brothers. I went to them in Salt Lake with my husband, Will. I married, Lizzie, I have a daughter and three sons, but they're all grown now and Papa is dead and Will is dead too, my husband, and I want you to come live with me—"

The interpreter tried to keep up with the torrent of words. Mrs. Brokenhorn gazed at her, puzzled, listening to the interpreter's translation and trying to grasp her relationship with the strange and disturbed white lady.

Then Mrs. Cook's words faded and she stopped speaking, like a mechanical toy running down. Mrs. Brokenhorn and her husband talked together briefly and then to the interpreter.

He turned to Mrs. Cook. "She says she can't go with you, Mrs. Cook. This man is her husband and this is her home. She wants to stay here."

"Oh, no," Mrs. Cook moaned. "Lizzie, listen to me, you don't belong here. I promised Mama I'd take care of you. Please come with me. Please, you're my sister. You're not an Indian!" She waited tensely as Mr. and Mrs. Brokenhorn talked again with the interpreter. He turned back to her.

"I'm sorry, ma'am," he said. "She understands she is a white woman, and maybe your sister. But she just won't go with you."

For the first time, Mary Cook broke into tears. She covered her face with her hands, but regaining her composure, she dabbed at her eyes with a handkerchief and drew herself up straight.

"Is there nothing I can do to persuade her?" she asked.

"I don't believe so, ma'am."

"Then I'll go." She turned a clear gaze on the other woman. "Good-bye, Mrs. Brokenhorn.... Lizzie." The interpreter escorted her through the village and helped her into the buckboard. A commotion caused them to look back.

The Indians were clustered around the Brokenhorns, shouting and laughing. Mrs. Brokenhorn strutted back and forth, talking loudly, pushing the squaws aside.

"What are they saying?" Mrs. Cook asked.

The interpreter could not admit that they were imitating and making fun of Mrs. Cook. "Well," he began, "Mrs. Brokenhorn says she's been an Indian almost all her life, but you reminded her she's a white woman also." Mrs. Cook looked away sharply. He added, "Maybe it'd be easier if you forgot your sister, Mrs. Cook."

"My sister," she said in a bitter tone. "That woman is no more than the ghost of my sister. I'll have to believe my little sister Lizzie was killed by the Cheyennes thirty-five years ago. That's what they told me then. I'll go home to my family now."

✿ *After the Civil War, when surveyors arrived on the Great Plains, the Indians were puzzled to see them measuring the land. It was like some exotic ritual.*

". . . The Indians used pegs for their tepees. But these men were not putting up tents. They were setting their 'stick-stucks' all over the prairie. It was as if they staked some huge, invisible tent to cover all the land."

These words, from a biography of the famous law officer Bill Tilghman, suggest the tenseness of the situation young Tilghman found on the southern plains in the winter of 1873–74. Nineteen years old, a brilliant marksman, an experienced frontiersman, he made his living at that time hunting buffalo and wolves for their hides and trading with the Kiowas and Cheyennes for the few additional buffalo robes they could bring him.

In those years the buffalo were being slaughtered by white hunters so carelessly, in such millions, that the vast herds were sharply diminished. Indians felt the pinch. The buffalo controlled their way of life; it was to them the greatest gift of God, the source of food, clothing, shelter, tools. In a study of Plains Indian culture, one writer lists over two hundred uses the Indians made of the buffalo.

The United States government authorities encouraged hunters to trespass on Indian lands to destroy the buffalo the more quickly. In that way, the In-

dians could be starved into submission and sooner forced onto reservations. Then their lands could be thrown open for speculators and settlers; surveyors could lay out farms and townsites. The tribes felt they were captives in their own country, trapped in an invisible tent the white men had staked out.

✺ CHAPTER SEVEN

"Stick-Stuck"

Billy Tilghman liked to sit in the Kiowa tepees, trading with the women, or smoking and talking with the men, or watching the children play. He liked the children best, liked hearing them laugh, watching them strut and wrestle. But the women of the household shooed them away when a guest arrived. A visiting trader was brought into the lodge and offered a bowl of food, and after eating he conducted his business, sometimes for many pleasant hours. On a day late in the autumn of 1873 the food was a thin stew, the chunks of meat in it mostly gristle. Still, Kiowa hospitality required that the guest be fed.

He sat cross-legged in the tepee of the Kiowa chief Kicking Bird, his friend. Kicking Bird's wife, having fed him, brought out her buffalo robes to trade.

One by one she took them from the rawhide case and spread them in front of him. He saw immediately that each was a full, fleecy hide tanned so perfectly that the leather side was like velvet to the touch. She hesitated

Buffalo grazing on the prairies.

before pulling out the last one. As she unfolded it Billy saw why. Not only was it the most perfect robe of the lot, it was an heirloom, a family treasure. The inner side was decorated with a complex sunburst design painted with exquisite skill in subtle earth colors.

She was a shrewd bargainer, this squaw. For the half dozen plain robes she accepted trade blankets, some knives and cooking pots. For the painted robe common trade items were not enough. She would exchange it only for a supply of food for her family. Billy got up and went out to his wagon with her.

She took a side of bacon, a bag of corn meal and another of beans, packets of coffee and sugar, as casually as if she were shopping at a grocer's in Dodge City. She was too proud to admit her family's need for this quantity of food; it was better to impress the white boy-trader with the great value of the painted robe. Besides, her husband had befriended him, and she felt he ought to be generous.

As he stowed the robes in his wagon, Billy studied the tepees clustered along Two-Hatchet Creek. It was almost like a ghost village. The autumn sky was bleak but the weather did not account for the atmosphere of tenseness and brooding in Kicking Bird's camp.

No children were laughing.

That was it. He heard no toddlers shouting, tumbling in and out of tepee openings. No ten-year-olds were breaking a colt or playing warrior games. Billy realized that in the months he had been coming to trade in the Kiowa and Cheyenne camps south of Wichita and Dodge City the children had grown long faces and hungry eyes. The few he saw drifted away, quiet and unsmiling.

Bill Tilghman as a young buffalo hunter.

Kicking Bird's Village, where Bill Tilghman went to trade.

When Kicking Bird came he led Billy back into his
lodge, lit a pipe, and they smoked and talked. Kicking
Bird, Tené-Angop'te in Kiowa, was a man of peace and
foresight whose melancholy eyes and gentle voice belied
the firmness with which he arbitrated between the reservation agents and his own people. He was trying to get
all the Kiowa bands to settle on the reservation near Fort
Sill and give up war parties and other old ways that
made trouble.

"Not many buffalo robe?" Kicking Bird said. He knew
Bill had been trading with his wife.

[126]

Kicking Bird (Tené-Angop'te), the Kiowa chief.

"No, Kicking Bird," Billy said. "Not many this trip. I'll have to go to trappin' wolves again to make a living. If I can find enough of them."

"White man come, animals go. Buffalo almost gone now." He was well aware that his young white friend had hunted professionally for the past two years, shooting thousands of buffalo for their hides, leaving the carcasses to rot on the prairie, and that earlier still he had killed hundreds more to supply meat for the railroad construction gangs laying rails across Kansas—across the heart of the buffalo range. Billy felt the rebuke of the chief's words.

"White man calls it progress, Kicking Bird."

"White man progress no good for Kiowa. Too fast." It was a point Billy could not argue. In the three years he had been on the plains, the railroads and settlements had created a new white man's world there.

When he was sixteen and on his first trip west, along the old Santa Fe Trail, Billy had been incredulous at the quantity of game, not just the endless herds of buffalo blackening the plains as far as the eye could see, but ducks and geese so thick they hid the water in the river shallows, prairie chickens, quail, plover and snipe, deer and rabbits everywhere, every thicket full of possums and raccoons, every streambank alive with beaver, otter, muskrat, mink. And always the coyotes and the big gray wolves trailing the buffalo to pick off a strayed calf. For thirty years, since the great migrations began in the 1840's, white men crossing the prairie in wagon trains had been killing and driving away the game, and now the hunters and railroads and settlers were finishing the job.

A young warrior burst into the tepee, shattering the

reminiscent musings of Kicking Bird and his white guest. An urgent conversation—then Kicking Bird sent the messenger out to summon the chief men of his band to a council. They soon came in, ten or eleven older men, the subchiefs. Before he realized what was happening, Billy found himself in the midst of the council. But no one objected to his presence. They went on with their business and ignored him.

Among the chiefs was Maman-ti, Sky-Walker, the great owl medicine man of the Kiowas. A tall man, lean, straight-backed, dignified, and powerful-looking, he was a war leader as well as a medicine chief. An owl's head dangled at his throat and he carried an owl-feather fan. Like Kicking Bird, Maman-ti knew that compromise with white men was inevitable, but unlike his fellow chief he wanted to resist, to hold out as long as possible. He was guardian of the ancient wisdoms of the tribe, keeper of the potent owl medicine that made the Kiowas successful in war.

In the place of honor at the back of the lodge Maman-ti sat next to Kicking Bird. The young warrior whose message had brought on the council followed the others in. Once all were settled around the fireplace, Kicking Bird signaled the young man to tell his story.

Billy did not understand much Kiowa but the messenger gave the story in such explicit detail that it was easy to follow: A small group of white men traveled slowly about the prairie with a wagon, not hunting, but performing a sort of ritual with strange metal instruments and flat sticks. One of these men would peer through a black tube mounted on three long sticks—here he made a tripod of twigs to demonstrate—then make medicine signs with his arms and shout, "Stick!" Then another man some distance away would tap one of his flat sticks into the earth, stand up, and shout, "Stuck!" They appeared to be pegging down a huge square tent that no one could see.

To substantiate the tale for his skeptical elders, the young warrior pulled out of his shirt an eighteen-inch-long stick of polished wood, the top battered from being hammered, the sharpened bottom end covered with dirt.

"Stick-stuck!" he said, holding it up. He gave it to the chief next him and it passed on around the circle. Billy leaned forward to see. It was a surveyor's marker.

When everyone had examined the stick it was handed back to Maman-ti. If some bad medicine emanated from it, it was safest in his hands. Maman-ti had great power.

Immediately the whole story came into focus for Bill Tilghman. Eighteen months before, while hunting buffalo for the railroad crews, he had ridden over a prairie swell and been confronted with a party of surveyors laying out the pattern of a town in an expanse of bluestem grass that grew as tall as a horse. It was startling to come upon the busy crew surrounded by the endless stretch of prairie. He had called out to them, "What'll it be, Kansas City or Chicago?"

"Likely big as both of 'em once it gets settled up," a surveyor had answered. "Lots of folks movin' out this way. Call it Dodge City." And there in that empty spot on the buffalo range Dodge City had grown into a thriving town.

Billy saw why the Indians were fearful of those stick-stuck men. Maman-ti too, in his wisdom, understood the fear, and explained it to his tribesmen.

"Bad medicine for us," he said. "These white men look like good men. They do not hunt buffalo. But over all our land they make their medicine. Their brothers have taken our hunting grounds and our buffalo. With stick-medicine they will try to drive us to a reservation now." Holding the stick out in front of him he snapped it in two and tossed the pieces in the fire. Chiefs and warrior pulled back, frightened, but no white man's devil rose up out of it. Stick-stuck power had already been released across the prairie. Hoarse-voiced, bitterly, Maman-ti said again, "For us, this white man's medicine is bad!"

Maman-ti rose and left the tepee, stroking his owl-feather fan. The others followed, all save Kicking Bird who sat gazing across his lodge fire. Through the tepee flap he saw the great leaden sky and under it the land he loved, but he saw the land emptied of buffalo, surrounded and closed off by white men. Winter gathered across it now, and for his people spring as they had known it would not come again.

Seeing the distant look in Kicking Bird's eyes, Billy Tilghman hesitated before taking leave of the chief. His encounters with Indians had been mostly pleasant. This emotional reaction, this withdrawing, was new to him. He felt uneasy. He wanted to leave with a smile and a light, friendly comment, but his nineteen-year-old frontiersman's cocksureness was gone for the moment. A little sheepishly, he climbed into his wagon and drove off. The council had given him much food for thought.

During the winter, Billy and his partners, Jim Elder and Hurricane Bill Martin, worked out of their camp near the Arkansas River south of Dodge City. They poisoned wolves and shot the few buffalo they could find. It wasn't a very profitable winter—clearly the old free life of the white hunters and plainsmen and Indian traders was not what it had once been. Hunters had to range farther and farther into Indian country to find any game to hunt, and the Indians had little to trade.

Besides, Bill found the Indians more edgy every time he went to one of their camps. Chiefs who had been friendly to him, like Kicking Bird and White Deer of the Kiowas, or Little Robe of the Cheyennes, were aloof and distant. Their young men were restless and rude to him, and paraded openly in their war gear. Among whites there was talk of Indian raids into Texas. Whether the

Little Robe, the Southern Cheyenne chief.

raids took place or not, Texans and the army used the talk as an excuse to kill many Kiowas, and take many horses from them. Early in 1874 the whole Kiowa tribe was in mourning for its lost warriors. The camps echoed with lamentations. Kiowa leaders vowed revenge.

And during that winter, Bill Tilghman came to feel that a change was due in his way of life. It had been a good life, but there was no longer much future in a hunting career, or as a scout or guide. He had had the best of Plains life—his boyhood dreams of adventure out west had been made real.

Adventure had turned out to be work, sometimes hard and sometimes dangerous. He had been very proud of himself when he got his contract with the Atchison, Topeka and Santa Fe Railroad to supply meat for their crews laying the tracks west of Hutchinson. He was only eighteen that spring of 1872, but already a full-fledged professional hunter, and probably the youngest working in Kansas. He persuaded his friend George Rust to join him and they had set out, trailing buffalo herds, shooting forty or fifty cows a week to provide the three thousand pounds of meat required. Their victims had to be cows, as the workmen complained that meat from buffalo bulls was too tough to eat. After the shooting had come the much harder work of butchering, and then hauling the meat in their spring wagon back to the workmen's camps. They left the hides to rot and stink on the prairie.

They fulfilled the contract to the perfect satisfaction of the ATSF commissary. Their shooting fed several hundred railroad builders throughout the summer. In September the contract ran out: the rails had reached Dodge City, as far as they were to be laid that year.

Buffalo hides ready for shipment from Dodge City, Kansas, in 1872.

Billy had expected to be out of a job in the fall of '72, as the railroad men were. But his skill as a marksman was still in demand. There was a new business, hide hunting, provided by the new rails. Leather and fur dealers in the east wanted buffalo hides and robes, and now there were trains to carry great quantities of them, as many as the hunters could get—summer hides for machinery belting or wherever heavy leather was required, winter skins for carriage robes and winter overcoats. Hunters who wanted to take time to cut out the tongues could salt and pack them in barrels for additional profits, and the buffalo's forelock of long coarse hair was also salable.

So the great buffalo hunt went on. Competition was heavy; Billy and his partner were only two among hundreds of hunters. The meat suppliers of that summer became hide hunters in the fall. Bill bought a second wagon and team of mules and hired two buffalo skinners to go out with them. The wagons were loaded with minimal food supplies, dried apples and beans, molasses, corn meal, coffee, and maple sugar—buffalo meat would be the

[134]

staple of their diet—and with kegs of powder, since like most hunting outfits they planned to load their own shells. They pulled out of Dodge City northwest along the Arkansas River. It wouldn't do to cross over to the south side. That was Indian country according to the treaty the army had made at nearby Medicine Lodge Creek back in 1867, and in '72 the Tilghman outfit was still hunting legally in country already taken from the Indians.

It was in his hide-hunting days that young Tilghman first met Indians. When the U.S. Army began encouraging hunters to push down into Indian Territory, Bill was one of the many who took up the offer. In the country south of Fort Dodge he shot his first animals and his skinners were just cutting into the hides when a dozen Indians, apparently friendly, rode up to them.

Seeing how the whites were occupied, they dismounted, shook hands, and the leader, a handsome man in magnificently embroidered buckskins, gave Bill a letter, which read:

> *The bearer, Little Robe, chief of the Cheyenne, is a good Indian. He has been to Washington and is a friend of the government. He has authority to arrest any white hunters found trespassing in the Indian territory, and to deliver them to the commanding officer at Fort Supply.*

The Cheyennes reached for the hunters' rifles, assuming they would submit to arrest. But Billy, with angry eyes and a curse, threatened them with his fists—he was a big boy, heavy-muscled and obviously powerful—and

[135]

he and his crew pulled their revolvers to keep the Indians at bay. Little Robe and his warriors quickly gave up the appropriated rifles and soon understood that their medicine paper from Fort Supply was worthless. The army had changed its tune and no white hunters were going to let themselves be arrested anywhere.

Well, those days were gone forever, he knew. The prairie was a changed place, thick with white folks' settlements. Where towns like Dodge City had mushroomed, he could remember bellying up to a herd, hearing the sound of their grunting as they cropped the rich prairie grass like a continual rumble of thunder in the distance. It was good to see towns and farms sprout up from the trackless wastes of grass. That country had been good for nothing but feeding buffalo, and buffalo only fed the Indians who worried new settlers. Soon they would be gone altogether, buffalo and Indians both.

As spring came on in 1874, Bill and his fellow hunters Jim Elder and Hurricane Bill Martin were busy at their camp on the Arkansas bundling their buffalo hides and wolf skins for the trip to Dodge City where they would sell them. Before they left, however, they made a scouting jaunt a few miles southward. A local rancher had offered them five dollars a head to find some of his cattle that had strayed into Indian country. On a fine April morning they started back with the cows they had rounded up. Meadowlarks streaked upward from the grass ahead of their horses. Off to one side of the trail and high in the blue Bill noticed buzzards circling, then dipping down. Something was wrong over there, something he should find out about. He turned his horse off the trail.

A few hundred yards' ride brought him to the remains of a camp. Just the remains, looted, burned, and ripped to pieces.

The cooking fire had been spread to catch the tent and a wagon loaded with supplies. Papers, clothing, and equipment were scattered all over the campsite. The body of a man lay among the litter. He had been scalped.

Young Tilghman stood up in his saddle and called, "Jim, Hurricane . . . come over here. Bring that camp spade with you." Dismounting, he chucked some pebbles at the buzzards. They flopped clumsily into flight and continued to circle the destroyed camp as the boys buried the body.

A broken instrument had been tossed aside in the grass. Bill picked it up to examine its crushed tube and polished wood parts. A surveyor's transit. Nearby lay a neatly tied bundle of flat wooden sticks, ready for use.

Stick-stuck!

He saw again the council of chiefs in Kicking Bird's tepee and the warrior describing how the white men made their medicine over the prairie: "Stick-stuck . . . ." He heard Maman-ti again, saying, "For us . . . bad medicine."

The three boys remounted and rode on toward Dodge.

This attack on the surveyors' camp wasn't likely to be the last of its kind, Bill knew. But at least such depredations were happening more rarely. The army of U.S. soldiers and the army of white hunters pretty well had the Indians cornered. A man could feel safe almost anywhere in Kansas. The railroads reached all the way across the plains. Towns and farms dotted the grassland. It was safer every day to take a government claim, throw up a sod house, and go to farming. Or you could set up your busi-

ness in a new town. Wichita was booming, so were Hutchinson, Ellsworth, Hays—and now this new Dodge City.
The frontier itself was clear past the Colorado line.

The boys rode through streets crowded with drifting
cowboys and bullwhackers, soldiers from Fort Dodge,
railroad men, out-of-work buffalo hunters, and emigrants
passing through town. At the railroad yards they found
the warehouse of Rath and Wright, hide buyers, and sold
their season's catch, then plunged into the crowd again to
enjoy the sensations of civilization.

Jim Elder and Hurricane Bill went back to the plains
a few days later for a summer hunt. But Bill Tilghman had
made up his mind that he was in Dodge City to stay. He
was twenty years old that summer, and his courage and
skill with a gun were in demand again, this time for pur-
poses of keeping peace in Dodge and protecting its citi-
zens. When he was offered a job as deputy sheriff, he took
it without hesitation, and as an officer of the law he found
a career that would sustain him for a lifetime.

✣ *By the mid-1870's losses of life and property in Indian attacks on the Plains had become a rare occurrence, which accounts in large part for the notoriety given the misfortunes of John German and his family. It was a useful story in two ways: the military could use it to justify their methods against the Indians and their continuing presence on the Plains at a time when respect for the army was waning, and it was a good story for popular entertainment. Such tales were great favorites in the popular press and the melodramatic theater of the day. The Indian was becoming a painted stage villain. Frontier families loved to read and retell them. One could thrill with horror and cluck the tongue in sympathy. After all, one of the fondest myths of the American frontier is that the white man's "heroism" was due to the constant danger (usually imaginary), of his being attacked and captured, scalped or killed by savage Indians.*

Another familiar myth, that of the white man's superiority and power over Indians (similar to the Nazi myth of Nordic infallibility), led John German to start his family, carelessly and in ignorance he could easily have avoided, on a trek across Kansas when the heavily publicized war of 1874 was ravaging the western plains. The lone German family in a single wagon set out from the last frontier town across a long stretch of prairie known to be the haunt of hostile Indians of several tribes, all defen-

[139]

sive in the extreme because they were being driven to the wall by a ruthless white army bent on their extermination. It was the sort of adventure undertaken not by heroes but by fools.

☼ C H A P T E R E I G H T

Farewell, Cheyennes

From her vantage point in the lead wagon, Catherine German turned, clinging to her seat, for a view of the procession trailing across the wintry prairie. It was a bumpy ride in the army carriage, called an ambulance, in which Catherine sat with her sister Sophia and the Cheyenne men who had been their guardians.

"Look," Catherine said. "Look there, sister! All on account of us." Sophia turned to see. The Cheyenne men did not.

At first glance there was something festive about the parade, but the subdued attitudes of the riders kept it from having a real holiday air. Harness jangled cheerily in the crisp air of early spring, saddle leather creaked, the wheels of the army wagons rumbled. Their personal escort rode close to the ambulance the girls were in, and the rest of the blue-coated cavalry was strung out on either side of the column of Cheyennes who marched between them, warriors proud and silent on their ponies, women wrapped in plaid or striped blankets, children whispering together, casting fearful glances at their

[140]

guards. Most of them had never before been so close to the hated white pony soldiers.

These Southern Cheyennes, the bands of Chief Stone Calf and Grey Beard, had surrendered themselves and their two white captive girls to the soldiers and had agreed to go peacefully to the Cheyenne-Arapaho agency at Darlington, Indian Territory. There they would give up their weapons and horses and freedom, and would be given food and become reservation Indians.

When the train halted for a midday break on the first day of the trip, the officer in command of the escort came to Catherine German. "Ma'am," he began in a confidential tone, "if you can, I wish you'd point out to me any of these redskins that was in the attack on your family. Any that was there an' run off with you girls."

Catherine German.　　　　　　　　　*Sophia German.*

Catherine was puzzled. It was so long ago, the trip in the covered wagon from Missouri with her parents and brother and five sisters. She and Sophia had traveled about and seen so much with the Indians since her father's wagon was burned and they were taken away. Now that she knew the Cheyennes well it was hard to remember which ones had been there that day of fright and confusion.

"Please try, Miss German," the officer added. "We want to bring 'em to justice, you see."

Catherine remembered not to point with a finger. Instead she pointed with her chin as a Cheyenne girl would do. "Well," she began, "him, I think . . . and him, and I guess that one." It was difficult to remember definitely, but she wanted to show her gratitude to these soldiers who had rescued her and Sophia. After living with the Cheyennes for five months the warriors didn't look at all scary to her any more, as they had on that misty September morning when they rode down on her father's wagon, hooting and screaming.

The guidons fluttered and snapped in the early spring breeze as the escort re-formed and the girls settled themselves in the ambulance. The train moved on. From time to time Catherine or Sophia would think of another who might have been in the attacking party and would point him out to the officer. Before the procession reached the agency, the girls had identified sixteen men.

Catherine felt it was important for her to be as cooperative with the army men as possible, and to appear as grown up as she could. She was seventeen years old, the oldest member of the German family left alive. It was up to her to be mother now, to twelve-year-old Sophia and to Julia and Addie, her two baby sisters who had already been recovered from the Cheyennes. She ached with impatience to see them again. But riding in this caravan was fun too, while it lasted. It made you feel very important, like a princess sort of girl in a book, with all her followers marching behind her.

On the second day of their winter trek, late in the afternoon, a shout of distant voices reached them. In the ambulance the Cheyenne chiefs talked in subdued tones

Julia and Addie German. This is the photograph with General Miles's message written on the back.

and gazed far ahead across the prairie. An officer rode up to them to say, "The whole garrison's out to welcome you girls back. Hear 'em?"

Another far-off shout floated over the brown landscape. As their wagon rolled to the top of the next rise Catherine and Sophia saw the buildings of the settlement. For nearly half a mile soldiers were lined up on either side of the road leading into it. They shouted, they cheered, they waved caps and handkerchiefs to the girls, and they turned ugly looks on the Cheyennes. The Indian prisoners were halted by their guards outside the area of the agency buildings.

Agent John D. Miles, in charge of the Southern Cheyenne and Arapaho Indians, and Colonel Thomas Neil, commander of troops at Darlington, came out to receive the girls. To their dismay they found Catherine and Sophia German crying heartily, unable to talk, apparently overcome by the confusion of their welcome and, the men assumed, relief at being among their own kind again. They made no attempt to interview the girls then, but put them in the hands of Joshua Trueblood and his wife Matilda, Quaker people who conducted the mission school at the agency. Hot baths, a good meal, and warm new dresses put an end to their tears. Catherine folded the cotton dresses the Indian women had made for them into a neat bundle, but their moccasins the girls still wore.

After the meal they stood gazing out a window at the bustling activity of the agency. Several wagons were being driven from a warehouse building to the spot where the Cheyennes had set up their tepees. Quantities of food were unloaded and distributed, whole sides of beef, bags of coffee, sugar and flour, enough to make one good meal for the hungry Indians.

"Is that bringing them to justice like the soldier said?" Sophia asked.

"I guess it is," Catherine said. "Anyway, it's the ransom they got for giving us up."

A soldier approached the missionaries' house, smiling when he saw the girls in the window. He brought the message that Chief Stone Calf had requested permission, and Colonel Neil had given it, for the Cheyennes to give a dance in honor and farewell to Catherine and Sophia. In a little while more soldiers came to escort them to the Indian camp.

A ring of troops was stationed all around the Cheyenne encampment. No Indians were allowed to enter or leave. The two German girls were brought in to the center of the tepee circle where a big soft heap of buffalo robes had been placed for them to sit on while they watched the dance. Two drummers had already started playing their tom-toms, some dancers tried a few steps, a warrior began to chant a song. Catherine noticed, as the dance progressed, that the blue-coated soldiers on guard drew together and fingered their rifles nervously. Never having seen an Indian celebration, they assumed all dances were war dances. Sophia and Catherine could have told them better. This was a peaceful celebration totally unlike the war and victory dances they had seen during their captivity, marked by hair-raising screams and whoops and pantomimes of attacking the enemy.

As they sat watching, a kind of farewell ceremony began. Girls and women of the tribe who had taught them the tasks of a Cheyenne household and taken care of them and been their friends came by ones and twos to say good-bye.

Each good-bye was more tearful than the last. The women embraced them, said a few words, and went away sobbing. Soon Catherine and Sophia were weeping too. It had been a difficult five months, but the Cheyennes had treated them well on the whole, as well as their means allowed, and strong bonds of affection and respect were established between the two girls and their Indian guardians.

The last woman to come was Wasita, Catherine's foster mother. Tears ran down her cheeks as she approached the girls on their throne of buffalo robes. Catherine handed Wasita the bundle containing the dresses the Indian woman and her companions had made for the two white girls, and she burst out with more tears and great wailing sobs. She threw her arms around Catherine and then Sophia, sobbing on and on at the Cheyenne's loss of their adopted white daughters. Finally other weeping women led Wasita to her tepee. The girls heard her lamenting long after, even when they were in bed at the mission school, her cries mingling with the happier sounds of the drums and singing.

Wasita and her people had reason to weep. They were seeing the last of something more than two little white girls they had grown fond of. Never again would they range the southern plains in their old free way. The morning after they danced for Catherine and Sophia German, the Cheyennes were required to stage a formal ceremony of surrender to the United States Army. The German girls were out early to see the great parade, standing with

Agent Miles and his wife and Mr. and Mrs. Trueblood before the agency administration building. Looking between the stiff-backed figures of the guard, they could see the Cheyennes coming from their camp.

First rode Chief Stone Calf with his guard of young warriors on their finest ponies. The lead man carried an enormous white flag. Then Grey Beard and other chieftains came riding, and all the men young and old, all painted and splendid in their most magnificent garments. Last were the women and children, and every member of the tribe was dressed in his most elaborate and beautiful clothes. As they dismounted, soldiers took away from them all the horses, saddled and bridled, all shields, spears, arrows, bows, knives, guns, and ammunition. It was an honorable and peaceful surrender. The Southern Cheyennes were a beaten people.

A mutter of satisfaction passed through the white soldiers and civilians. The Cheyennes were herded together and taken back to their lodges. The soldiers took their stations; the circle of tepees was a prison camp.

"Miss German?" Colonel Neil, having settled the Cheyennes, wanted to finish the business of their captives.

"Yes, sir?" Catherine answered.

"You can help us, Miss German, if you feel up to it now, by telling how these Indians attacked your family and how they treated you and your sisters."

Of course she felt up to it. She had used up her current supply of tears in the past few days and felt refreshed and prepared for the interview. She sat in his office with Colonel Neil and told him the story straightforwardly and unemotionally.

The German family of nine—parents, a son, six daugh-

[147]

ters—came from Georgia. Conditions were so bad there after the Civil War, Catherine remembered, that her parents wanted to move west. First they went to Tennessee, then to Missouri, then Kansas. They were on their way to Colorado, but they would stop in places for a few months so that Catherine, her older sister Jane, her brother Stephen, and their father, John German, could earn money to take them farther west. In Missouri they settled on a homestead, but their farm was a failure so they exchanged the claim for a team of oxen and a wagon to travel in. Late in the summer of 1874 they set out on the last long lap to Colorado, from Elgin, Kansas, where they had been working for the past ten months.

What Catherine remembered best was the coop of Sophia's chickens hung on the back end of the wagon, and the cow with two calves that she and Stephen had charge of. The wagon rolled on northwest to Ellsworth, then due west along a trail next to the Kansas Pacific Railroad tracks. Near Ellis, Kansas, they took the old stagecoach road which paralleled the Smoky Hill River. For eighty miles there were unlimited water and grass for their stock and idyllic camping spots. On September tenth, the Germans camped no more than a day's journey from Fort Wallace. The younger children argued about whether Colorado was close enough to see from the fort.

At sunrise on September eleventh, John German, carrying his old army rifle, walked ahead of his oxen as they pulled the wagon out of camp. Mrs. German sat on the front bench with Sophia and Joanna while Julia and Addie, only five and six years old, rode on a feather bed inside. Jane, the eldest, was in the wagon with them.

Stephen and Catherine herded the cow and calves behind the wagon.

Suddenly, silent as a vision in the misty morning light, a herd of antelope broke across their trail a few yards ahead. Then, Catherine said, before her father or her big brother could get a shot at the vanishing antelope, the Germans heard war cries and the beating of ponies' hooves, and they were inundated in the whooping swirl of Cheyenne warriors.

John German died first, then his wife as she jumped from the wagon to join him. Jane leaped to the ground swinging an ax, hit two Indians and was shot down by a third. Stephen and Catherine, in panic, ran away from the wagon. The boy was shot immediately and fell dead. An arrow grazed Catherine's leg and stuck in her skirt, but an Indian pulled it out and dragged her back to where her sisters were. Joanna was killed and scalped for her long hair. The two little girls were pulled screaming from under their feather bed in the wagon and kept with Sophia and Catherine. Addie's loud crying annoyed a warrior, who threatened to shoot her, but an energetic little squaw bustled forward and claimed her, thus saving the child's life. Other Indians were looting the wagon and driving off the cattle. There were nineteen in all, two of them women.

To Catherine, the whole attack seemed to last only a few minutes. Then the four girls were pulled up onto horses and carried away. Their wandering captivity had begun.

The attackers were of two different Cheyenne bands. Addie and Julia, the two younger girls, were taken by the

[149]

woman who had saved Addie from being shot. They were not allowed to be with Catherine and Sophia, who had been claimed by two braves, and one day in their southward wandering the little squaw, her husband, Julia, and Addie rode away with the Indians of their band and were not seen again. Catherine later came to believe the little girls were dead.

"You know your sisters are fine now, Miss German," Colonel Neil interrupted. "At Fort Leavenworth. They were with the Cheyennes only a few weeks."

"Yes, sir," Catherine said. "I've heard . . . I'm so anxious to see 'em."

"We'll send you up there soon as we can."

Catherine, while still a captive, had learned how Julia and Addie were recovered. A cavalry troop attacked a small Cheyenne camp on November 8, 1874, and when the skirmish was over found that the Indians had purposely left the little girls sitting on a buffalo robe where the soldiers would find them. They had been taken to Fort Dodge and then to Leavenworth where they were put in the care of Patrick Corney, the fort's blacksmith, and his family.

The two older girls, meanwhile, had been taken to a large Cheyenne village in northwestern Texas and did not yet know of their little sisters' rescue, or that their family's bodies had been found and that they themselves were the subject of a search by the military in its constant offensive war against the Plains Indians. Sophia and Catherine, weary of traveling, were unaware that the Indians' reason for moving about so much was to elude the endless pursuit by soldiers. It was a relief to be settled for a while in

Cheyenne tepees. Meat is drying on the racks at center; lower right, a little girl's play tepee with her mother's plaid shawl for cover.

the large village of Chief Stone Calf near the Pecos River in eastern New Mexico. Sophia had been given to a widow and her old mother, members of the band of a chief called Grey Beard. Catherine was claimed by the squaw Wasita and her husband, of Stone Calf's band. They made her understand that they intended to be *ni-ho-e*, father, and *na-ko-e*, mother, to her.

[151]

They had not been badly treated, Catherine felt. The work required of them was not hard—mostly tedious domestic chores like wood- and water-carrying, no harder than similar work they had done all their lives. Occasionally Wasita, in a burst of temper, would whack at Catherine with a lariat, but the girls were not otherwise beaten or abused. Catherine was given a man's flannel shirt to wear over her Indian dress and both girls had blankets. The only real discomfort, which they shared with the Cheyennes, was hunger: as the winter wore on rations grew short. Because of harassment by the army, the Indians could not safely go far from their secluded Pecos River camp to hunt, and the buffalo and other game were scarce and wary.

Catherine was of course old enough to be teased and followed by the young men. Once when traveling the band came to a small river, and the boys pretended to threaten her with a ducking. She earned their respect by leaping in and swimming calmly across. Later, Wasita thought to make a profit by offering her to a young brave, but when he came to Wasita's tepee with the intention of making Catherine his bride, she fought him off like a tigress. After that the young men did not trifle with her.

In January, 1875, Stone Calf brought Catherine a short letter from General Nelson Miles. She was as impressed at being addressed by the general—who was then as famous an Indian-killer as Custer—as she was by the information that he was negotiating for her and her sister's release. A few days later she was delighted by a second message scrawled on the back of a photograph of Julia and Addie taken at Fort Leavenworth. *These Germain sisters are well and are now with their friends,* he had scribbled hastily. *Do not be discouraged; efforts are being made for your benefit.* Signed with a flourish, *Nelson A. Miles.* As she had done with the letter, Catherine raced off to Grey Beard's village to share the good news with Sophia.

Two weeks later, in mid-February, Chief Stone Calf led his tribesmen on winter-weakened ponies across the snowy plains toward the Cheyenne Agency. Seventy-five miles west of Darlington, the army escort met them, and after final negotiations led the procession on eastward. An army ambulance had been sent. In it Catherine sat between Chief Stone Calf and her foster father, her *ni-ho-e.* Then Sophia joined them with her guardian, a man called Bear Shield. And so, in a great parade across the prairie, Catherine and Sophia German returned from their captivity among the Southern Cheyennes.

Life at the Darlington agency was calm in the spring of 1875. On the twenty-first of March there was a little celebration for Catherine's eighteenth birthday. The girls had letters from their grandfathers in Georgia; they had an army visitor, a Lieutenant Baldwin, who told them the details of their family's burial at Monument, Kansas; and they had many Indian visitors. Stone Calf came, and Bear Shield and other friends, always with gifts. Forty fine buffalo robes were given them, and four mules, and all these were sold so the girls could have money for new clothes and for living expenses.

Otherwise, few incidents ruffled the routine Sophia and Catherine had fallen into. Late in March they were taken

[153]

to the Indian prison camp and asked again to identify men who had been present in the attack on their family. This time they could be sure of no more than three or four.

The army authorities believed the others had escaped a few days before. There had been a skirmish between guards and Indians: twenty-five men were selected to serve five-year prison terms at Fort Marion, Florida, and one of them, while being shackled with a ball and chain, tried to break away. He was shot dead. The soldiers panicked and began shooting into the tepees. The Cheyennes—except for the prisoners already shackled, of course—ran into the sand hills nearby and defended themselves with a few guns they had hidden. That night they succeeded in slipping away to the camps of their relative bands, those of Chiefs Little Robe and Whirlwind, a few miles down the Canadian River.

All this shooting didn't affect Catherine and Sophia. They were in the mission school at the time. They continued at the agency until June 1875 and then, as Colonel Neil had promised, an army escort took them to Fort Leavenworth, Kansas, where they rejoined their sisters and were taken into the lively family of Patrick Corney, the blacksmith. Newspaper reporters came to interview them and made their story well known. And General Nelson Miles did not forget the girls. He took time off from Indian-chasing to persuade Congress that $10,000 should be taken out of the Cheyennes' annuity money for their benefit. The interest on this money was used for their education and maintenance until they came of age, then the principal reverted to them. In 1878, Patrick Corney moved his entire family, including the four German sisters, to Wetmore, Kansas. It was a pleasant town to grow up in.

☼ *Indian life was imbued with religious thought. From birth to death, and before and after them, every act of living was charged with some godly spark and subject to divine control. And one's religion was not personal and private: the relationship of man and God was celebrated in great public observances. Festivals like the annual Sun Dance of the Plains tribes brought the scattered bands of a tribe together —thus renewing and maintaining the unity of the people—to perform elaborate rituals of supplication and thanks to the deity for supplying the people with the needs of life.*

With the disintegration of tribal life brought about by the Indian Wars and the adjustment to life on reservations, it became increasingly difficult to practice the old faith. There was a constant pressure from the whites to give up traditional beliefs; in some cases, notably with the Sun Dance of the Kiowas and the Ghost Dance, performances of the rituals were stopped by the military. But there were those among the older generation for whom the white man's ways and beliefs could never really replace the faith of their fathers.

CHAPTER NINE

The Ugly Kiowa

The three little boys—the ugly one and his two friends—stopped playing when they heard screams of terror from their village. They had built a play fort on the outskirts and played their imaginary war with the gringos within sight of their parents' adobe shanties, which baked in the midsummer sun of northern Mexico.

The screams and shouts stopped their play, and they saw the grownups vanish into the houses. Now there was only silence. In the adobe huts some men loaded rusty muskets and others pulled out machetes, while terrified women clutched babies to their breasts. The only villagers to be seen were the three boys. Their terror-stricken parents had forgotten they were outdoors.

The smallest boy screamed out a long piercing wail when he saw the Indians ride slowly down the dusty village street. His older brother, speechless with fright, grabbed his hand and ran with him, looking for a place to hide.

But the ugly boy stepped forward, hypnotized. "Indians!" he whispered. "Beautiful!" He stared in awe, but without fear, as the seven Kiowas rode toward where he stood in the road from the village. A couple of the warriors laughed at him as their ponies idled past. A grin of delight illuminated the ten-year-old boy's chubby monkey face. But the Kiowas did not stop. There was nothing to stop for in this poverty-stricken village. The boy's grin faded as he watched them ride on.

"Indians, wait!" he called. "Take me with you!"

One of the Kiowas halted and looked back, puzzled by the chattering, pleading boy who ran up to him. "Please! Let me come with you, please," the child begged. "Teach me to be an Indian." He pleaded and gesticulated until the warrior finally understood, pulled him up behind him on the pony, and spurred the animal to a gallop to join the others. They were riding northward to their home on the Staked Plains. It was the summer of 1859; in seventy years of life with the Kiowas the boy never asked to return to his Mexican home.

The ugly little boy wanted to be an Indian. He never found any reason to leave his adopted people, even after their tribal life was shattered and they were confined to a reservation. His name was probably Joaquin, but for Kiowa tongues it was easier to call him Mo-keen, the name he bore to the end of his long life. As a very old man, Mo-keen recalled the dry and barren country of Chihuahua, but he would not talk about it much. He preferred to leave his origins forgotten in the silent squalor of a Mexican village. Happiness and fulfillment came for him in the rich tribal life of the Great Plains.

When the Kiowa braves rode into their camp in northwest Texas, the people crowded around to see the one prize, other than a few horses, of their expedition. The prize, ten-year-old Mo-keen, sat proudly behind the warrior he rode with, pointing, exclaiming, grinning in delight at everything he saw. He looked like nothing so much as a happy young ape.

The warrior dismounted and set the boy down. Children stared and Mo-keen grinned back at them. When the squaws poked at his plump body, he giggled. A happy and unfrightened captive was something new to them. The brave led him up to an old man and began talking about him.

Mo-keen listened carefully to their conversation. The sound of the Kiowa tongue pleased him. He knew he would learn it quickly. Through gestures, the brave made it clear that he was to follow the old man to his lodge, so the boy trailed off after him. But he looked back wistfully at the warriors. Some day, he thought, I will be a warrior, too.

However, Mo-keen's life was to take a different turn than he expected. The old man he had been given to was Aun-so-kat-tauh (Old Man's Foot), one of the chief medicine men of the tribe and priest of the Sun Dance. Aun-so-kat-tauh adopted Mo-keen as his own son, treated him kindly, and raised him in the strict tenets of his religion. He had plans for the boy's future.

Life in the camp was paradise to young Mo-keen. He was a cheerful, clever child and the Kiowas soon came to love him. Their language is a difficult one for outsiders to learn, but within a few weeks he could chatter freely with them. He threw away his ragged trousers and shirt and Aun-so-kat-tauh gave him a breech clout to put on his chunky brown body. His curly hair grew long and his olive skin darkened in the Texas sun. He ran and wrestled with the Kiowa boys, herding ponies with them and learning their games. They taught him to ride as they did, to gamble as all Indian boys learned, and to shoot with a

[159]

small bow and arrows. Soon he was bringing home doves and quail, a rabbit or gopher or other "small deer," as they called little game.

But Mo-keen was not to grow into a warrior, as he had wished at first. Aun-so-kat-tauh saw to that. He wanted his son to follow in his steps, to learn and carry on the beautiful traditional rituals of the Sun Dance.

Mo-keen came to agree with his foster-father. Fascinated with the dramatic rites of the religion, he became a devout believer and proved himself the perfect apprentice to the old medicine man. When Aun-so-kat-tauh died, Mo-keen, although still in his teens, became the Keeper of the sacred Tai-me idol, the priest who guarded it in his tepee and took it from its buffalo hide case to display during the Sun Dance services.

Long before the great gathering took place, the people talked about and planned for the Sun Dance festival, which was held in early summer. It was a reunion of the whole tribe for sociability and entertainment, but more than that it was a rebirth and strengthening of tribal solidarity through the medium of a great religious observance.

A model of the Tai-me, the sacred medicine doll of the Kiowas.

Excitement mounted as the scattered bands gathered at the site selected for the great medicine lodge and the preparatory rituals began. There were prayers to the sun, there was a carrying of the Tai-me before the people by the Tai-me Keeper, there was the ritual hunt for the young buffalo bull, part of whose hide would be hung on the center pole of the great lodge. When the hide was brought in to camp all the people sang the "Buffalo-Coming" song and then hung their offerings of seashells or feathers or bits of bright cloth on it.

One of the most exciting events was a wild sham battle charge, by all the tribe's warriors, on the tree that was to be the center pole of the lodge. Everyone cheered the warrior who first touched the tree and then it was cut down by a woman captive. As the warriors carried it to the site of the medicine lodge it was halted four times and Mo-keen would run from its base down the whole length balancing like a tightrope walker. It was bad luck for everyone if he slipped off before reaching the forked end. He wore only a breech clout and rabbit fur cap, his body was painted white, and in his mouth was a whistle made of an eagle's wing bone. When the center pole was set in its place, the brush walls and roof of the lodge were built around it, the inner floor spread with clean sand, and the Tai-me was placed in a sanctified area facing east.

The next morning at dawn the Sun Dance began. Forty dancers painted white, wearing caps and wristlets of sacred sage, danced facing the Tai-me in its white feather garment and necklace of blue beads, danced for the favors of the sun who would enrich the earth to feed the buffalo and so sustain the Kiowas.

For four days and nights the dancers continued with no food and hardly an interval for rest. Mo-keen observed and guided the rituals of the dance throughout its course. On the fourth evening he brought it to an end and there was a general dance and song by all the people celebrating the blessings of the sun and the earth. Next day the tepees came down and the bands separated to go about the business of living for another year.

Although his religious duties prevented him from training as a warrior or becoming a member of a warrior society, Mo-keen was not excluded from socializing with the young braves. He rarely went on war parties with the other young men of the tribe, yet there is evidence that he did go at times. He is known to have been on a raid in 1864, when he was fifteen years old, in which a little white girl named Millie Durgan (who like him lived the rest of her life with the Kiowas) and a group of Negro slaves were captured.

Most Kiowa boys married young. Perhaps Mo-keen's devotion to the Sun Dance was the reason he did not. Being so absorbed in the religion and his duty to guard the Tai-me, he may have had no time for girls. On the other hand, the reason may have been Mo-keen's looks. After all, the Kiowa maidens were looking for every young girl's ideal—a lad who was tall, lean, and handsome—which Mo-keen decidedly was not. He was short and stout, had curly hair and a very dark skin. The Kiowa girls found him so unattractive that none of them would have him.

When, as a mature young man, Mo-keen finally did marry, it was to the widow of Satanta, the famous Kiowa chief who died at the Texas state prison in 1875. Satanta's widow was called Zoam-tay (Born With Her Teeth), and Zoam-tay soon gave Mo-keen a son, Ait-san (Killed-Him-On-The-Sly). Mo-keen was the happiest of men. He was deeply attached to his son, and Ait-san was to have a profound influence on his father's life.

It was obvious, as Ait-san's quick, alert, and friendly personality developed, that he had inherited his father's best qualities. At the age of nine, chance brought him the beginnings of a formal education. A wandering Quaker schoolteacher, Thomas Chester Battey, set up a kind of school in a tent at the Kiowa village on Cache Creek. The children began learning the English words for birds and animals whose pictures Battey showed them.

But the lessons were destined not to last long. A jealous medicine man told the squaws that Battey's pictures were bad medicine. The children would die, he said, if they looked at them. Zoam-tay was at the head of a delegation of squaws who immediately descended on Battey's school-house tent and dragged their children away.

Ait-san had no further education until 1878, when he was fourteen. His mother died about that time and Ait-san begged Mo-keen to let him go to the Quaker boarding school for Indian children near Fort Sill. At first Mo-keen was very reluctant to let Ait-san go, but the boy begged so hard that his father gave in and took him to the school. A month later Mo-keen went back for him, sure that his son would be homesick and eager to return to the Kiowa camp.

Mo-keen was in for a surprise. He found that Ait-san loved the school, was a good pupil, and had made many friends. So Ait-san stayed. But the winter of 1878–79 was the school's last year at Fort Sill before it was moved to Anadarko. Now the boy was faced with a dilemma: his taste of education at Fort Sill had stirred his fine young mind, and he wanted to go on to school at the famous Carlisle Indian Institute in Pennsylvania. It was the great desire of his life, but he knew Mo-keen would have strong objections.

"Our ways are changing," he said to his father. "I cannot be a leader of warriors, but if I go to this school I can be a leader of another kind."

"No," said Mo-keen. "I have no wife, I have no other children. You cannot leave me now."

"But this will be a good thing for us both."

"No, Ait-san. If you leave me again and go so far away, I will kill myself."

Ait-san pleaded gently, trying to make his father understand what it would mean to him to go to Carlisle. Finally Mo-keen consented, but not willingly.

The great day of departure came. Ait-san piled into a wagon with ten other Kiowa boys and girls for the jaunt to Arkansas City where they would catch the eastbound train. Mo-keen began to cry. He embraced his son and prayed, "O sun, look upon my boy and let me see his face again." As the wagon pulled away, his tears flowed again, sobs racked his stout body. Ait-san could hear him crying until the wagon was far from the camp.

Ait-san was right about the changing of tribal ways. The tribal life Mo-keen had known as a boy had almost vanished. The Kiowas were now settled on the reservation near Fort Sill and the younger people were looking out for new ways of life. It was Mo-keen and the other older men who tried to cling to the good old ways. To make a living, however, Mo-keen had taken a job driving freight wagons. For almost twenty years, he and his Kiowa friend Hunting Horse were two of the best-known drivers in Indian Territory, with a run extending as far north as Arkansas City and south to Henrietta, Texas.

For a couple of years after Ait-san went to Carlisle, Mo-keen lived alone as a widower, driving freight wagons in the outside world and teaching the lore of the Sun Dance in the Kiowa camps. But loneliness grew too much for him and he remarried, this time to a woman called Sait-mah.

It was not a very happy marriage, although the couple did have one child, a beautiful little girl. However, when the little girl died, Sait-mah ran away from Mo-keen with a warrior called To-yope.

Mo-keen was enraged at his wife's faithlessness. His first thought was to track down the runaway couple and punish them. Revenge would be sweet. But he was an aging man and not a warrior: he could not do it alone. It was best to revert to the old tribal ways. He invited several Kiowa men to his lodge to smoke a pipe with him before explaining the favor he wanted to ask of them. They came reluctantly, not wanting to get involved in a family quarrel, but once they had smoked with Mo-keen they were obliged, according to Kiowa custom, to help him.

Mo-keen led the men out on his search. At one point they met a train of Mexican traders on the prairie. Yes, they said in answer to the Indians' questions, they had

[165]

seen a Kiowa man and woman traveling, and in a hurry. They described Sait-mah and To-yope, speaking of To-yope (who was not remarkable for his masculine beauty) as the ugliest man they had ever seen until now, and they burst out laughing: Mo-keen, they said, was even uglier.

Mo-keen took their joke without comment. He was used to being described as the ugly Kiowa. Being an Indian had always been more important than the comments his bad looks drew from others.

The search party never found the runaway couple. But about a year later Mo-keen was one of a party of Kiowas who went to smoke a pipe of peace with the Cheyennes. By custom, peace could not be broken between the two tribes after the peace smoke. This made Mo-keen a victim of frustrating circumstances, since To-yope appeared next day in the Cheyenne camp. He and Sait-mah had been hiding with the Cheyennes, fearful of the anger of the Kiowas.

It was too late for revenge. Mo-keen and To-yope discussed the situation and made an honorable property settlement. Mo-keen went home a lonely widower, but richer by several horses and a saddle or two.

Mo-keen was an aging man now. Teaching and performing the Sun Dance rituals and lore to younger devotees occupied his free time. He was still Keeper of the sacred Tai-me, the idol wrapped up in its buffalo hide case, and guardian of its hallowed traditions. It became more important to him to preserve these traditions and keep alive the old religious spirit of the Kiowas, because the army authorities at Fort Sill outlawed the Sun Dance—not knowing its real meaning, they claimed it

[166]

stirred the Kiowas up to go out on the warpath or on horse stealing raids. The last Sun Dance was held in 1889.

More and more Mo-keen was feeling the effect of the changing ways. To curb his loneliness, he married again, this time to a woman named Paudle-kon-mi, but again he was frustrated because she died a couple of years later. However, the time came when Ait-san returned from Carlisle Indian School and Mo-keen was happy once again, as well as being very proud of his educated son.

One of the Kiowa girls who had gone to Carlisle with Ait-san was the daughter of Mo-keen's friend Hunting Horse. The white teachers called her Mabel. Mo-keen's son they had renamed Lucius Ben Aitsan. Soon after their return from Carlisle, Lucius and Mabel were married.

It was Lucius Aitsan who brought about the last turning point in his father's life. Lucius was a deeply religious young man, but not in the faith of his father. He and Mabel were baptized and became staunch members of the tiny Baptist congregation at Saddle Mountain in 1896, and Lucius became the first Indian pastor of Saddle Mountain Baptist Church, where he was ordained on June 24, 1913.

For years Lucius had tried to talk his father into giving up his faith in the Tai-me and the Sun Dance and becoming a Christian. Mo-keen held out, trying to resolve the doubts in his mind. One of the major stumbling blocks was finally resolved by the advice of his friend Hunting Horse.

"How can I be a Christian?" he said to Hunting Horse. "They say I must go in water to be converted."

"And the medicine of the Sun Dance forbids that," Hunting Horse agreed.

"My medicine forbids me to go in water or under

*Lucius and Mable Ait-
san, Mo-keen's son and
daughter-in-law.*

water," Mo-keen said, thinking of the immersions at the
Baptist church. "If I do I will die. That is the medicine's
power."

The two men sat in deep thought. At last Hunting Horse
spoke.

"Go ahead," he said. "Your son wants you to be Christian. You don't say no to being Christian, you only afraid
of water. But if you go in water and die, you must go
straight to heaven anyway. So go ahead."

This argument, along with Lucius' perseverance, won
Mo-keen over. He was baptized by immersion and
became, nominally, a Christian. But Mo-keen was torn
by the religious conflict. As late as 1918 he was still teach-

ing the Sun Dance worship, and he was to be haunted for the rest of his life by this splitting of his religious allegiance. The last tragedy of his life was, he felt, a punishment for his trying to hang on to both religions at once.

This is how the tragedy happened: Mo-keen had lived for several years in the home of his son and daughter-in-law a mile west of the Saddle Mountain Baptist Mission. One day he went out to a gathering on the reservation to teach some of his young disciples about the Sun Dance. It was a day's ride from home, and Mo-keen, after talking with the young devotees, was delayed from starting back by a violent thunderstorm which came up suddenly.

At home, Lucius Aitsan got caught in the same storm while out rounding up their horses and small herd of cattle. Soaked to the skin, he took to his bed with a serious cold. When Mo-keen returned the next day he found Lucius delirious with a raging fever. Mabel was weeping, frightened. It was a dangerous time, they knew, for anyone to get the least bit sick—the great influenza epidemic of 1918 was ravaging the country.

Mo-keen was shaken as he saw his son's burning, sweating body weaken. He watched the disease take over. For this disease, he knew, the old medicine would be no good. He went out to the corral and saddled a pony. But by the time he got back with the doctor, Lucius was dead.

It was almost more than Mo-keen could bear. He had lost three wives and his only other child. Now his son was gone, the mainstay of his life on whom he had lavished all his pride and love. All the gods seemed to have punished him, the pagan ones and the new Christian one as well. He was a broken old man.

[169]

The Kiowas began to call him "Man of Iron," because he was so tough and long-lived, and also because he was so bitter and outspoken, lashing out at everyone about him. Now he had nothing but memories left. He remembered the desolate, waterless land he had left as a child, the fine nomadic tribal life on the plains, the mystical beauties of the Sun Dance rituals he had so loved. He did not regret his voluntary captivity with the Kiowas: he could hardly have had a better life. He only regretted the loss of Ait-san, his fine son, and his own religious stubbornness, which he believed had brought on him the great punishment of Ait-san's death.

Finally the time of rest came for Mo-keen. He died in 1934, a man full of years—almost a hundred—and full of the experience of life. He was laid with his people in the Saddle Mountain Indian Mission Cemetery, not far from the church where his son had been the pastor.

Mo-keen.

✲ *The ugly and dishonorable history of the Indian Wars came to an end at Wounded Knee Creek, South Dakota, in the last days of December 1890.*

Government authorities had been trying to suppress the Ghost Dance religion, a revivalist cult that particularly attracted the starving and destitute northern Plains Indians. The religion taught peaceful living, nonviolence, nonresistance to white men. The devout believed that in time their faith and performances of the mystical Ghost Dance would bring back to life all the ghostly buffalo and Indians dead from white men's guns and diseases. One of the prayer songs said:

> *Father, have pity on me,*
> *Father, have pity on me;*
> *I am crying for thirst,*
> *I am crying for thirst;*
> *All is gone—I have nothing to eat,*
> *All is gone—I have nothing to eat.*

White men would vanish from the Great Plains and the old ways of life would come again. The hopeful dancers sang:

> *My children, my children,*
> *Look! the earth is about to move,*
> *Look! the earth is about to move.*
> *My father tells me so . . . .*

In the autumn of 1890, large contingents of troops were moved into the Sioux reservations in South

Dakota. The Sioux took this movement to be a war-like preparation. To avoid fighting, hundreds hurried to the ancient sanctuary of the Bad Lands. Farther north, at Standing Rock Reservation, white authorities believed the famous medicine man Sitting Bull was planning a revolt and using the Ghost Dance to whip up warriors' enthusiasm. The proud old man was brutally murdered by Indian police sent to arrest him. His followers, believing Sitting Bull's death to be only a prelude to their own destruction by the ever-threatening white soldiers, fled southward in panic, hoping to join their people in the safety of the Bad Lands. Intercepted by cavalry troops, they were forced to camp at Wounded Knee Creek on December 28th. There the band of about

The Ghost Dance of the Sioux.

340 Indians (of whom barely a hundred were warriors) were surrounded by five hundred heavily armed soldiers whose armory included four Hotchkiss machine guns aimed at the tepees. The warriors were drawn into a council at a spot away from the tepees and bully gangs of soldiers went to loot the camp of any arms they might find. When one warrior objected to giving up his guns, which he had at no time attempted to use against the troops, the commanding officer gave his men the signal to fire. Then ensued an orgy of butchery, somewhat bloodier but not unlike concentration camp massacres of more recent history.

All the Indians were slaughtered except for a handful of children. No attempt was made to aid the wounded; many died by fire when their tepees were burned over them, many froze to death on the ground in a blizzard that struck next day. Several days later a shallow trench was dug and the frozen corpses were dumped into it, most of them stripped naked by souvenir-hunting soldiers. The warriors' bodies were at the council spot, but some women's and children's were found as much as a mile from the camp where they had been chased and stabbed or shot to death by American soldiers. Missionaries of several denominations at nearby Pine Ridge Agency did not bother to come out with the burial party to say a service for the dead.

The American public accepted Wounded Knee as

a victory for the U.S. Army and a final settlement of the "Indian Problem" on the Plains. It was also popular as a spectacular scene in Buffalo Bill Cody's Wild West Show during his 1909 season. The mass burial was not included in the scene.

CHAPTER TEN

The Cowboy Kid

It was all over. After thirty years, Buffalo Bill's Wild West Show had come to an end, closed and sold at auction to pay the tens of thousands of dollars in debts owed by Colonel William F. Cody—Buffalo Bill himself. The only thing he had left from the show was his famous trick horse, Isham. An admiring friend had bought Isham for him at the auction. The old scout went off to his Wyoming ranch to recover from the blow, muttering, "The show business isn't what it used to be, Johnny."

Johnny Baker, the Colonel's foster son and arena director of the show, felt as if he were losing his entire family. He had supervised the staging of the acts, the entrances and exits and theatrical effects, but he was more than a show director to all the performers in those acts. To the Indians, cowboys, sharpshooters and trick riders, and the roustabouts and stagehands who put it together every day, Johnny was their advisor and guide, champion of their rights, nursemaid and fatherly friend. Now, with the failure of the show, those relationships were broken. The last performance was played at Denver in July, 1913, and there was not even enough money to pay the performers their salaries. They were set adrift, looking for jobs in other shows. The Indians wandered back to their reservations. Johnny went home to North Platte, Nebraska, hoping he could find some way to help the Colonel get back on his feet.

Since he was fourteen years old, Johnny Baker had traveled with Buffalo Bill's Wild West. Colonel Cody, utilizing the boy's uncanny talent for marksmanship, billed him as "The Cowboy Kid, Champion Boy Shot of the World." His life was spent as one of the star marksmen of the show (along with Annie Oakley), and in later years as its arena director. Now, in the autumn of 1913, all the excitement of touring and performing in towns all across America and Europe was at an end.

But Buffalo Bill, even at sixty-seven years of age, had no intention of giving up show business, and Johnny was ready to join his foster father in any project he proposed. "I'll just have to start life over again—with no capital," the Colonel said.

He kept Johnny posted on his thinking with a stream of letters, each one offering another new scheme for getting back into business and making fortunes like those he had made and lost in his Wild West Show. Every plan except one seemed too complicated or impractical, but that one made very good sense.

A new form of show business called motion pictures was sweeping over the country. The jerky images flickering across screens had come to be a serious competition to the Wild West Show in its last couple of seasons. People would rather pay to see this new novelty than to see a real

[175]

Johnny Baker as The Cowboy Kid, Champion Boy Shot of the World in Buffalo Bill's Wild West Show.

Johnny Baker as a young man.

live show. Well, why not join the competition, Colonel Cody said, and make motion pictures of famous events in western history that everybody would want to see. They could film the Battle of War Bonnet Creek including Buffalo Bill's duel with Yellow Hand, and maybe the Wounded Knee affair. Both had been great hits when done as scenes in the Wild West Show.

The Colonel and Johnny were fired with enthusiasm. In a few days they were at work. Hurrying to Denver they talked with the Secretary of War, who happened to be there at that time, and who gave his permission for the use of real troops and the Indians at Pine Ridge Agency in South Dakota. Several prominent army officers offered to appear, as a favor to their friend Cody, in scenes of battles in which they had actually fought. They remembered him as young Buffalo Bill, scouting for their troops.

A deal was made with the Essanay Film Company to supply cameras and crew, and "The Col. W.F. Cody (Buffalo Bill) Historical Pictures Company" came into existence. Men were sent off to scout the Sioux reservation for photogenic locations near Pine Ridge and set up cameras and equipment.

When Johnny and the Colonel arrived, the Indians had set up their village on Wounded Knee Creek, not far from the Pine Ridge Agency and near the site of the famous massacre. Here most of the filming would take place. Short Bull, Iron Tail, and others who had been with Buffalo Bill's show were present, so there was a pleasant reunion. But the tribesmen, they said, were uneasy about making a show of the place where their people had died and were buried. "Johnny'll set their minds to rest," the Colonel said, "when we get to that part."

The army camp was also laid out nearby. Six hundred men of the Twelfth Cavalry were the soldiers. The Quartermaster's Corps had come up with some old uniforms, so many of the men were authentically dressed in the period of the battles to be filmed. When General Nelson A. Miles arrived, he inspected the sites and soldiers to be photographed and gave strong advice on how to make historical motion pictures. He had come out of retirement and insisted that the pictures be absolutely authentic and accurate in every detail. More generals appeared on the scene. Soldiers and Indians milled about. The bustle and confusion were compounded.

[178]

PROGRAM

BUFFALO BILL (Col. W. F. Cody) U. S.
Government approved. Historically Correct.

Indian War Pictures

Cover of a program for Colonel Cody's Indian films.

"Johnny," Colonel Cody said, "it's time for my arena director to take over."

And Johnny went to work with the camera people, organizing the various contingents of Indians, soldiers, and officers to prepare for the film making. The first day's work consisted of introductory shots of Colonel Cody, one or two Indian leaders, and the famous army officers, including General Miles, Generals Charles King, Frank Baldwin, Jesse M. Lee, and Colonel Marion P. Maus. Everyone else looked on as, one by one, they saluted the camera. In the days that followed the troops and Indians were put to work recreating first the Battle of Summit Springs, which had taken place in 1869, and then the War Bonnet Creek encounter of 1876, during the course of which Colonel Cody energetically demonstrated for the camera, with a substitute Indian, how he had killed and scalped the famous warrior Yellow Hand in single combat.

Everybody was delighted at how well the work was progressing. Making motion pictures was a lark. It was almost like old times, with Buffalo Bill a kind of active figurehead, Johnny Baker directing arena activities, and soldiers and Indians acting out theatricalized versions of half-forgotten battles. There was even calliope music to add a circus atmosphere: a traveling carousel had set up shop just out of camera range. Only the live audience was missing, and shooting acts like the one Johnny Baker did, acts that alternated with spectacle scenes of Indians attacking wagon trains or burning settlers' cabins or fighting soldiers.

The Indians were much the same as always, showmen to the core, riding past the camera with war whoops and ferocious grimaces. After work they rode the carousel's wooden horses round and round with similar whoops and scowls. Nevertheless, Johnny sensed a current of unrest among these Sioux, something he could not put his finger on. Well, he thought, in time they'd tell him what the problem was. They respected Johnny for his frankness and calm disposition, and for a sensitivity and understanding of their problems that few other people had. He, in turn, had always felt close to them. In the show their scenes were the ones he most enjoyed staging and watching and offstage he found himself more in sympathy with their problems than with those of the white performers.

When the Wild West Show had played Rome in 1890, Pope Leo XIII received a group of Indians who were Catholic converts. One brave was ill, however, and stayed behind at the show grounds. On their return, the Indians were shocked and puzzled to find that he had died at the very time they were in the company of the man they took to be God incarnate. It was Johnny who restored their faith and persuaded them they were not all doomed, as

Sioux camp at Pine Ridge Agency, South Dakota.

they feared, for having left their Plains and crossed the great water.

It was easy, Johnny knew, to think of them only as show people because he saw them only in the artificial circumstances of theatrical life, just as it was easy for audiences to believe the myth created by shows like Buffalo Bill's and see them only as skulking, painted villains. It was easy to overlook the fact that they only took show jobs to escape the horrors of impoverishment and starvation on the reservations.

On the day the camera was moved from Pine Ridge to Wounded Knee, Johnny noticed again that they seemed ill at ease and uncertain. Many of the squaws were in mourning. When he began instructing them in their actions for the film, they were frankly uncooperative. While the camera was being placed, he looked for Short Bull. Thinking to draw the chief out, he said, "Would you rather work in an arena with a big audience?"

"Maybe better," Short Bull answered.

"Why's that, Short Bull?"

The Sioux chieftain considered carefully before speaking. "In show, all false. We pretend warriors. At Wounded Knee fight, real warriors died. Our people buried there." He pointed up the slope from the creek to where the bodies of his ancestors had been buried in the trough graves.

So that was it, Johnny thought. He should have known. The Sioux have so little left, at least the graves and the place where their people had been massacred ought to be left undefiled. On the other hand . . .

"Short Bull," Johnny said, "if the film shows the whole

[182]

fracas exactly the way it happened, then audiences will know it wasn't your people who started it. They'll find out the Sioux were in the right all the time."

"So. So," Short Bull said.

"You know, a lot of white people say the fight here at Wounded Knee was part of a big Indian plot, and the Sioux were planning a war."

"Not so."

"I know, but that's what people say. Don't you think your people who died here would want you to make these pictures so there's a true record of what happened? They say the camera can't lie."

The new idea struck a receptive chord in Short Bull, who immediately went to share it with his people. The first day of filming went well. Scenes were made showing the Sioux with their cavalry escort arriving and setting up camp at the creek, then the council scene where the warriors were asked to give up their guns.

But before the day came when the battle itself was to be filmed, General Nelson Miles, demanding literal accuracy in each scene, announced a decision that nearly stopped work altogether. Filming had already been slowed down by his insistence that brief scenes which had taken place in the Bad Lands had to be shot there, many miles away, although they could easily have been done in the hills around Pine Ridge. At one point he was determined to show all eleven thousand men who had taken part in the campaign of 1890: the six hundred soldiers available were marched past the camera again and again until he was satisfied, but no one told him the film had run out after the third time. Now the general

[183]

came up with his poser. After the fight was photographed, he said, the mass grave would have to be dug up and the burial scene recreated with dummy corpses.

No immediate comment was made. After the day's work the Indians went quietly home to their tepees, more quietly than usual. That night, Johnny Baker had a visitor in his tent. It was Iron Tail, one of the chiefs. Without preliminaries, Iron Tail let Johnny know why he had come.

"Sun come, trouble come," he said. "Young Sioux men crazy mad. They dress for war. They got real bullets. In battle for picture tomorrow, they kill white soldiers. You get Pahaska, we talk."

Johnny was already out of the tent. "I sure will, Iron Tail. You get your chiefs. Meet us in the dining tent."

Pahaska, as the Indians called Colonel Cody, came with Johnny as soon as the state of affairs was explained to him. He had left a conference with General Miles and the camera director, but dared not bring Miles with him, or even tell him why he had left. It was bad enough the Indians had real ammunition—there was no point in provoking them into using it that night.

In the dining tent he and Johnny sat drinking coffee. The chiefs, they knew, would confer among themselves before coming to them. It was after two in the morning when they finally filed into the tent and sat in a council circle. Iron Tail, No Neck, Short Bull, and other Sioux leaders were there, men who had traveled with the Colonel's show and been friends with him and Johnny Baker for years.

Cody spoke first. "I hear your young men got some live

[184]

ammunition," he began in a stern voice, without introduction. "Johnny here tells me they want to shoot up the soldiers tomorrow in that battle scene. Now why is that?"

Short Bull answered him. "Revenge, Pahaska. They get even on soldiers for our people who died here."

"But that's crazy," Johnny broke in. "Don't those boys know they'd never get away with it?"

"They got good ponies. They get away fast."

"They'd be killed before they got off the reservation. There're more soldiers here than there were at the real Wounded Knee fight."

The Colonel spoke again. "Now, Short Bull. Iron Tail. All of you. You are old men, wise men. Do you mean to set there an' tell me you can't ride herd on that bunch of fool young'uns? You speak for the Sioux, that's why you're here and not those crazy boys. You go tell 'em there'll be no shooting real bullets and no killing of anybody. It's an act, just like you done in my Wild West Show. In the show you chiefs told the young men what to do. How about doin' that now?"

The chiefs, embarrassed at his rebuke, looked at each other, then at Johnny. He turned to Cody. "They feel we shouldn't be doing anything like a show act here anyhow, Colonel. And I think maybe they're right. Wounded Knee Creek and that slope there is sacred ground to them, just like a churchyard is to us. You know, Colonel, I think it would settle things if you could promise them you won't let General Miles dig up the graves."

The Colonel considered. It would have been sensational, soldiers refilling the actual grave.... It wasn't worth arguing. "All right," he said. "I'll put my foot down.

[185]

General Miles nor nobody else'll touch those graves. We'll shoot the battle tomorrow and then clear the whole troupe out of Wounded Knee."

The chiefs rose, clearly satisfied. "Pahaska talk straight talk," Iron Tail said. "Young men will not shoot real bullets. Chiefs have spoken."

"So . . . so," Short Bull said, and the others grunted their assent.

"I'm glad to get this picture-taking wound up," the Colonel said. "Think I'll go out on the road with the picture show, give a lecture with it, maybe have an Indian museum in the theater lobbies, an Indian to do a little talk—Iron Tail, how about you? . . ." His voice droned on as they walked out into the chill autumn night.

Next morning, the Sioux, young men and old, came to Johnny for their instructions. They were agreeable, at least for that day, to being show Indians. Before long the air over Wounded Knee Creek was shattered with Indian war cries and soldiers' shouts, shrilling cavalry bugles, the banging of guns. Every gun was loaded with blank cartridges. The real bullets had been put away.

Dead Sioux lying in the snow after the massacre at Wounded Knee, South Dakota; the soldiers are collecting souvenirs from the frozen bodies.

Afterward, it was as if the whole camp of picture makers gave a sigh of relief. It had gone well. The massacre and burial of the Sioux at Wounded Knee was on film, and even General Miles approved the way it looked. Some of the Indians went for a ride on the carousel, punctuating the wheeze of its music with the last of their blank shots.

"Well, I'm glad that day's work is done," Johnny Baker said to Short Bull. "This business is harder on my nerves than being the arena director for two or three Wild West Shows."

"So. Now white men go," the chief said. "Pahaska make new show?"

"No, Short Bull, I'm afraid not. But if he did we'd sure offer the lot of you a job with it. Things aren't so good on the reservation, huh?"

"The Sioux are poor and hungry."

Johnny looked at the tepees strung along the creek bank. "And the people killed at Wounded Knee were poor and hungry. But shooting things up isn't the right way. Revenge for the dead doesn't feed the living, Short Bull. In the Ghost Dance, your people had songs about better times coming."

"Many years ago they sing. Not much better time now."

"But they're some better. Sioux and white live in peace now. You don't have to forgive, but forget revenge at least. And in time—well, time's a healer, they say."

"So. Maybe . . . ."

In a few days the confusion of people and cameras was gone. Calliope's music faded away. Soldiers were sent to their forts, old generals went back into retirement, and the Indians trailed off across the Dakota prairie to set up their winter camps. Under the snow that fell on the slope dead grass lay waiting for spring. Immeasurable sky and land were silent again, there was no sound save the wind blowing freely down the frosty plains, soughing across the graves at Wounded Knee.

For Further Reading

Andrist, Ralph K., *The Long Death*. Macmillan, 1964.

Brandon, William, et al., *The American Heritage Book of Indians*. American Heritage Publishing Co., Inc., 1961.

Chittenden, Hiram Martin, *The American Fur Trade of the Far West*. Academic Reprints, 1954.

DeVoto, Bernard, *The Course of Empire*. Houghton Mifflin Company, 1952.

———, *Across the Wide Missouri*. Houghton Mifflin Company, 1947.

———, *The Year of Decision*. Houghton Mifflin Company, 1943.

Grinnell, George Bird, *The Fighting Cheyennes*. University of Oklahoma Press, 1955.

Hyde, George E., *A Sioux Chronicle*. University of Oklahoma Press, 1956.

Irving, Washington, *A Tour of the Prairies*. University of Oklahoma Press, 1956.

Lavendar, David, *Bent's Fort*. Doubleday, 1954.

———, *Westward Vision, The Story of the Oregon Trail*. McGraw-Hill Book Company, Inc., 1963.

McNichols, Charles L., *Crazy Weather*. Macmillan, 1944.

Marriot, Alice, *The Ten Grandmothers*. University of Oklahoma Press, 1945.

Mathews, John Joseph, *The Osages, Children of the Middle Waters*. University of Oklahoma Press, 1961.

Mayhall, Mildred P., *The Kiowas*. University of Oklahoma Press, 1962.

Sell, Henry Blackman, and Victor Weybright, *Buffalo Bill and the Wild West*. Oxford University Press, 1955.

Skinner, Constance Lindsay, *Adventurers of Oregon, A Chronicle of the Fur Trade*. Yale University Press, 1921.

Trenholm, Virginia Cole, and Maurice Carlsy, *The Shoshonis, Sentinels of the Rockies*. University of Oklahoma Press, 1964.

Wallace, Ernest, and E. Adamson Hoebel, *The Comanches, Lords of the South Plains*. University of Oklahoma Press, 1952.

Wellman, Paul I., *Death on Horseback, Seventy Years of War for the American West*. J. B. Lippincott Company, 1947.

Index

[191]

[193]

THE AUTHOR

Gene Jones was born and reared in the West. He came east after he was graduated from the University of Arizona, to work in the theater in New York City and in stock companies on the road. However, writing has always been Mr. Jones' major interest. He began while he was still in high school and has done a great deal of editorial work and free-lance writing for magazines. *Where the Wind Blew Free* is his first book.

Mr. Jones, his wife, and son live in Cold Spring, New York.